COMPUTERIZED QUANTITATIVE INFRARED ANALYSIS

A symposium sponsored by
ASTM Committee E-13 on
Molecular Spectroscopy and
Federation of Analytical Chemistry
and Spectroscopy Societies (FACSS)
Philadelphia, PA, 18 Sept. 1984

ASTM SPECIAL TECHNICAL PUBLICATION 934
Gregory L. McClure, Perkin-Elmer
Corporation, editor

ASTM Publication Code Number (PCN)
04-934000-39

 1916 Race Street, Philadelphia, PA 19103

Library of Congress Cataloging-in-Publication Data

Computerized quantitative infrared analysis.

(ASTM special technical publication; 934)
"ASTM publication code number (PCN) 04-934000-39."
Includes bibliographies and index.

1. Infrared spectroscopy—Data processing—Congresses.
I. McClure, Gregory L. II. ASTM Committee E-13 on
Molecular Spectroscopy. III. Federation of Analytical
Chemistry and Spectroscopy Societies. IV. Title:
Quantitative infrared analysis. V. Series.
QD96.I5I66 1987 543′.08583 86-26534
ISBN 0-8031-0929-6

NOTE

The Society is not responsible, as a body,
for the statements and opinions
advanced in this publication.

Printed in Ann Arbor, MI
January 1987

Foreword

The symposium on Computerized Quantitative Infrared Analysis was held in Philadelphia, Pennsylvania, 18 September 1984. The symposium was sponsored by ASTM Committee E-13 on Molecular Spectroscopy and Federation of Analytical Chemistry and Spectroscopy Societies (FACSS). Gregory L. McClure, Perkin-Elmer Corporation, presided as symposium chairman and editor of this publication.

Related
ASTM Publications

Advances in Luminescence Spectroscopy, STP 863 (1985), 04-863000-39

New Directions in Molecular Luminescence, STP 822 (1983), 04-822000-39

A Note of Appreciation
to Reviewers

The quality of the papers that appear in this publication reflects not only the obvious efforts of the authors but also the unheralded, though essential, work of the reviewers. On behalf of ASTM we acknowledge with appreciation their dedication to high professional standards and their sacrifice of time and effort.

ASTM Committee on Publications

ASTM Editorial Staff

Helen M. Hoersch
Janet R. Schroeder
Kathleen A. Greene
Bill Benzing

Contents

Overview

Historical Perspectives

Chemistry is a science which has a middle position as both the server and the one served with respect to other disciplines. In addition, one can understand the special field of analytical chemistry as an important focal point of technology, from which many types of services to other sciences are delivered, and into which many of the developments in other fields are incorporated. The point of making this observation is to emphasize that Chemistry (and particularly Analytical Chemistry) acts as both the donor and recipient from the collective technical knowledge of man, which means that the field is subject to continuous change and rapid growth. The obvious consequence of this situation is that it is useful to make periodic assessments and reassessments of the so called "state of the art" in particular areas. This volume developed out of the awareness of the need to develop an accurate account of the current status of quantitative infrared methods of analysis, and to provide a clear presentation of the power of this technique in the context of modern computerized infrared spectroscopic instrumentation.

Much of the sense of need for this work was generated during discussions centered around revision of the ASTM Recommended Practices for General Techniques of Infrared Quantitative Analysis (E 168). It became apparent during the work on revision of E 168 that so much had occurred and was still occurring to change the nature of quantitative work in infrared spectroscopy that the revised E 168 could not include a comprehensive discussion of all areas of the topic. Consequently the E 168 work group narrowed its focus to generate a document which would deal with general guidelines and the most major of issues in quantitative infrared. To expand on the more complicated issues in greater detail, a symposium was planned, from which articles could be generated to form a separate, more lengthy publication. The symposium was organized and held at the 1984 annual meeting of the Federation of Analytical Chemistry and Spectroscopy Societies (FACSS) in September in Philadelphia, Pennsylvania. The symposium was cosponsored by FACSS and ASTM. Additional financial assistance was provided by Digilab (subsidiary of BIO-RAD Corp.) and is gratefully acknowledged.

1

It is somewhat ironic that infrared spectroscopy started its industrial scientific life as a quantitative tool. One of the first commercially produced infrared spectrometers was codeveloped by scientists working during the early 1940s at American Cyanamid and Perkin-Elmer, to handle the problem of characterizing styrene-butadiene polymers in the defense related issue of synthetic rubber production. In the following decade gas chomatography replaced infrared in many quantitative industrial applications, and infrared was generally relegated to the task of molecular identification. The loss of favor by infrared with respect to quantitative applications could be easily understood in terms of the relative difficulty in carrying out the analysis with the instruments of the era. Not only was there a question concerning ordinate and abscissa reproducibility in the spectral data, but the result of instrument operation was just an ink trace on a piece of paper. This left the analyst with the task of measuring transmittance values with a ruler and calculating absorbances and concentrations with a slide rule or desk calculator, or even just a piece of graph paper.

The introduction of the double beam infrared spectrometer provided a simpler and more aesthetically pleasing spectrum from which to work, but it did not alleviate the basic difficulties involved in obtaining a reliable quantitative result without excessive effort or tedium. Moreover, the optical null double beam instruments introduced an additional source of error in terms of the uncertainty of the location of the zero transmittance point, and this caused some concern among analysts.

Major changes occurred in the seventies. Some of the important factors were incorporation of microprocessor technology into infrared instruments, development of desk-top microcomputers, and the evolution of Fourier transform infrared (FT-IR) spectrometers into reliable, powerful and affordable instruments for measuring spectra at high signal to noise ratios, even with relatively low transmittance samples. There were two subtle factors which shaped the progress of infrared quantitative analysis during this era. The first was that FT-IR instruments required their own integral computing system to produce spectra from interferograms by Fourier transformation. This meant that spectroscopists and analytical chemists obtained, often for the first time, a powerful computing device of their own which was not dominated and controlled by outside personnel from industrial computing centers. Coupled with this was the fact that vendors of FT-IR instruments provided some additional software besides the Fourier transformation algorithm, which allowed easy transmittance-absorbance interconversion, spectral subtraction, and even computerized quantitative routines.

During the same period dispersive instruments experienced substantial improvements, major among which was the development of the microprocessor controlled ratio recording infrared spectrometer. Among the advantages of the ratio recording systems was that an accurate measure of the zero percent transmittance point could be obtained. In the late seventies microcomputers began their rapid incursion into scientific laboratory instrumentation. Often these systems were called anything but computers, in an effort to enhance their chances of being retained under the auspices of the laboratory personnel rather than those of the companys' computing center. However, before the end of the 1970s, it appeared that no serious instrument vendor would consider designing a product for the future without providing for internal or external computing facilities. This set the stage for the arrival of the age of computerized quantitative infrared. Infrared instruments had improved to the point that the data were generally accurate and reproducible, and small computing devices were attachable or built internally which could evaluate the spectra and calculate the results automatically with methods that could be designed and tailored by the laboratory chemist.

One further development that should be mentioned is the declassification of the now commonly available mercury-cadmium telluride (MCT) detector. This device was originally developed for military purposes, but eventually was declassified and found its way into use in FT-IR instruments of the chemical laboratory. The MCT detector is operated at reduced temperatures by cooling with liquid nitrogen. It can produce high signal to noise spectra at low light levels, and is most favorably operated at high signal modulation frequencies (for example, 10 to 100 kHz). In contrast, dispersive infrared spectrometers (which generally use thermocouples) and FT-IR spectrometers fitted with room temperature deuterated triglycine sulfate (DTGS) detectors operate best at lower signal modulation velocities. For example thermocouples are operated in the general range of 10 to 100 Hz while DTGS detectors on most FT-IR instruments are operated around 1 to 2 kHz. The result was that FT-IR instruments fitted with MCT detectors showed some substantial speed advantages over dispersive spectrometers. In addition, publications appeared which described the use of FT-IR spectrometers with MCT detectors to provide some spectral subtractions even at low light levels which appeared nothing short of miraculous. Manufacturers took advantage of continued developments in electronics and computing hardware to provide FT-IR instruments at prices competitive with computerized dispersive instruments. As a result of all of these factors FT-IR developed into a buzz word and a fad which infected the analytical laboratory, and generally foretold the end of the dominance of dispersive infrared instruments except for the lower cost units.

The impact of all this on quantitative infrared is that it also foretold the virtual end of infrared instruments without the availability of data handling facilities. FT-IR, a necessarily computerized form of laboratory instrumentation, had set the standards by which all infrared work would be measured. This meant that there was substantial generalized pressure that laboratory infrared instruments would be computerized even if they were dispersive systems. As a consequence, laboratory infrared instruments would be capable of carrying out quantitative applications with a maximum of reliability and a minimum of tedium and effort. This situation gradually developed into a major revival of interest in the possible uses of quantitative infrared for industrial analytical applications. The factors mentioned contributed strongly to the development of interest by a number of people working in the field, in the updating of the ASTM standard E 168 on General Techniques of Infrared Quantitative Analysis and also ultimately to an interest in the generation of this volume on Computerized Methods of Infrared Quantitative Analysis.

Summary of Technical Papers

The papers included in this compendium were derived from or are related to the presentations made by some of the authors at the 1984 ASTM-FACSS symposium on Computerized Methods of Infrared Quantitative Analysis. One of the values of this type of publication is that each of the authors provides a somewhat different perspective on the entire field based on his own unique experience and area of particular interest. It is hoped that this volume will not only provide interesting and informative reading in the short term, but that it will also be of use in the long term, as a useful desk reference for those who are likely to be involved in development of quantitative infrared applications in the present and future.

The first paper by Osten and Kowalski provides an interesting critical review of the developments in infrared quantitative analysis through the year 1984. Many significant references are cited, and this organization of the developments in the field should facilitate the work of future reviewers of progress in this field, and also those who wish simply to appreciate the strides that have been made thus far.

The second paper by Compton, Young, Kollar, Mooney, and Grasselli describes a number of applications related to petroleum products and makes some practical recommendations concerning the development of analytical applications. The third paper by Willis, Chalmers, Mackenzie, and Barnes is also heavily applications oriented and deals with applications which illustrate the modern use of quantitative infrared in the synthetic polymers industry.

The next group of three papers are focused on the use of computerized techniques to carry out multicomponent analysis by infrared methods. These papers give useful discussions of the mathematical aspects of these applications for those who are interested. The paper by Haaland describes an approach to dealing with nonlinear absorbance/concentration relationships with multivariate techniques such as the **K**-matrix method. Crocombe, Olson, and Hill describe some important aspects of multivariate calibration and compare the **K**-matrix and **P**-matrix methods. The paper by McClure, Roush, Williams, and Lehmann deals with the application of the **Q**-matrix method to the analysis of a multicomponent system with a high degree of spectral overlap.

The paper by Malinowski presents the essential aspects of using factor analysis in quantitative spectroscopic applications. At this point, the techniques associated with factor analysis are still in the relatively early stages of incorporation into general use in quantitative infrared software. However, it can be foreseen that factor analytical techniques in some form will play a much heavier role in quantitative infrared software developed in the future.

The final paper by Hirschfeld emphasizes the need for caution and cross-checking in the use of computers for spectroscopic determinations. The same sentiment is echoed throughout the preceding papers, but the case for caution is made most strongly by Hirschfeld with some interesting examples to illustrate the point.

It is with deepest regret that we note the passing of our highly esteemed colleague, Tomas Hirschfeld, on 24 April 1986. He was a source of inspiration as well as information to all of us. Although he clearly remains with us through his work, he will be deeply missed by all of us. I am sure all of the authors will join me in dedicating this volume to Tomas, a scientist, colleague, and friend.

Gregory L. McClure
Perkin-Elmer Corporation, Ridgefield, CT
06877; symposium chairman and editor.

David W. Osten[1] *and Bruce R. Kowalski*[1]

Multicomponent Calibration and Quantitation Methods

REFERENCE: Osten, D. W. and Kowalski, B. R., **"Multicomponent Calibration and Quantitation Methods,"** *Computerized Quantitative Infrared Analysis, ASTM STP 934*, G. L. McClure, Ed., American Society for Testing and Materials, Philadelphia, 1987, pp. 6–35.

ABSTRACT: A systematic examination of calibration and quantitation methods available to analytical chemistry is made. First, simple linear calibration with one sensor is reviewed with an emphasis on chemical problems that can invalidate calibration models and what can be done about them. Then, a shift is made to multivariate methods used for multicomponent analysis ending in a discussion of bilinear forms.

KEY WORDS: bilinear forms, calibration, chemometrics, multicomponent analysis, multicomponent calibration, multicomponent quantitation, multivariate analytical methods, multivariate calibration, multivariate quantitation, quantitation, sensor calibration, sensor error

The general problems of calibration and quantitation are well known to analytical chemists. The traditional approach to quantitative analysis often has been to find a single sensor which was specific for the desired analyte and responded in a linear manner to changes in the analyte concentration. The requirement of a fully selective sensor frequently necessitates various separation or purification steps prior to the analytical measurement. An alternative approach is to use many analytical sensors and multivariate data analysis methods. The objective of this review is to provide the reader with an overview of multivariate calibration and quantitation methods known at the time this symposium was held in 1984 and to discuss some of the assumptions inherent in applying these approaches to analytical measurements.

Analytical Chemistry has recognized the importance of this problem by establishing a report on Chemometrics as a part of its biennial *Fundamental Reviews* issue. Sections of the past Chemometrics reviews entitled "Modeling and Parameter Estimation," "Calibration," and "Resolution" are of particular interest to researchers in this area [1,2].

[1] Graduate student and professor, respectively, Laboratory for Chemometrics, Department of Chemistry, University of Washington, Seattle, WA 98195.

This review is grouped into three distinct sections. The first section containing a review of the single-component linear model will provide the basis for development of the more complex models, such as the multicomponent linear model in the second section. The latter is based on one-dimensional response measurements; for example, the absorption spectrum of a mixture sample. The third section will discuss the multicomponent bilinear model. This model can be used to describe two-dimensional chemical measurements such as fluorescence excitation-emission matrices, gas chromatography-mass spectrometry (GC/MS) data, liquid chromatography-ultraviolet (LC/UV) data, or spatial/spectral data as obtained from imaging in surface analysis.

Single Component Linear Model

The situation most favored by analytical chemists is when the response, r, of a single analytical sensor is a linear function of the concentration, c, of a single chemical analyte of interest.

$$r = kc \tag{1}$$

In order to obtain an estimate of the analyte concentration, two general steps are required. First there is a calibration step, in which the sensitivity coefficient, k, is determined based on the analysis of one or more samples of known concentrations. The second is a quantitation step, in which the response of the unknown sample is measured and the analyte concentration is estimated from the calibration model. Implicit in using this simple linear model is a series of assumptions about the chemical system being examined: first, the response is linearly related to the analyte concentration over the concentration region of interest; second, the analytical sensor is fully specific and responds only to the analyte of interest; and third, the sensitivity coefficient does not change between the calibration and quantitation steps. If these three assumptions are obeyed for a given experimental situation, then the calibration line is obtained by measuring the response at various analyte concentrations [3].

Since the analytical sensor is fully specific, the response of a sample containing no analyte is by definition equal to zero. This implies that the calibration line must pass through the origin. In principle, measurement of a single sample of known analyte concentration is sufficient to determine the slope of the calibration line. In practice, several measurements are preferred. Even in situations where a theoretically linear relationship is known to exist, the measured experimental values will rarely be co-linear with theoretical values due to sample variance, measurement errors, and random noise.

Random Error

The method of least squares is commonly used to estimate the position of the calibration line. The mathematical formula for calculation of the least squares regression line and the confidence region around this line are well known [4,5]. Several additional assumptions are required when the method of least squares is used to estimate the calibration relationship [6]. The first assumption is that all the measurement error is associated with the dependent variable, the measured response. This condition requires the variance in the concentrations of the standard samples to be much smaller than the variance in the corresponding measured responses. Secondly, each measured response is drawn from a normal distribution with a mean equal to the true response for the corresponding analyte concentration. This requires that repeated measurements of the response for a single sample yield a Gaussian distribution. Lastly, the variance of the measured response must be independent of the analyte concentration, or in statistical terms there must be homogeneity of variances.

If M-calibration samples have been analyzed, with each calibration sample being measured one or more times such that N total calibration measurements were made, then the calibration step requires estimating the values of two parameters; the slope, β_1, and the intercept, β_0, of the least squares line. For the single-component linear model, the least squares problem can be expressed as minimizing the sum of the squares of the residuals in the following vector equation

$$r = \beta_0 + \beta_1 c + \epsilon \qquad (2)$$

where

r = a column vector containing the N measured responses,
c = a column vector containing the N known analyte concentrations, and
ϵ = the vector of residual errors not fitted by the model.

Shewell [7] has observed that varying the location of the calibration points will have an effect on the accuracy of the estimates obtained for the slope and the intercept of the regression line. In general, for a constant total number of calibration measurements, $N,$ the most accurate estimate of the intercept, β_0, is obtained if $N - 1$ measurements are made at the lowest permissible analyte concentration and one measurement is made at the highest permissible analyte concentration. If the most accurate estimate of the slope is desired, then the measurements should be equally divided between the highest and lowest permissible concentration levels.

Agterdenbos [8] considered the effect of altering the concentrations of calibration samples on the precision obtained in the final concentration estimate. Both the distribution of the calibration measurements over the concentration range of interest and the number of replicate measurements were found to influence the results obtained in the subsequent quantitation step. A new quantity, the eccentricity, can be defined to describe the relationship between the precision of the estimated sample concentration and locations of the calibration points. The precision of the estimated sample concentration, Δx, is a function of several parameters: the selected statistical significance level, t; the standard deviation of the analytical procedure, s; the total number of calibration measurements, N; the number of replicate measurements of the sample, n; and the location of the sample measurement in the calibration range or the eccentricity, E.

$$\Delta x = 2\ ts(N^{-1} + n^{-1} + E)^{1/2} \tag{3}$$

The eccentricity, E, can be calculated from the following relationship

$$E = (\hat{\bar{x}}_s - \bar{x})^2 \Big/ \sum_{i=1}^{N} (x_i - \bar{x})^2 \tag{4}$$

where

$\hat{\bar{x}}_s$ = mean estimated analyte concentration, and
$\bar{x}$ = mean concentration of the calibration samples.

From these relationships it is clear that the minimum uncertainty in the estimated analyte concentration will occur when the sample concentration is equal to the mean concentration of the calibration samples, in which case the eccentricity is equal to zero. As the sample concentration moves to a value further from the center of the calibration plot the eccentricity increases and the precision of the estimated sample concentration becomes poorer.

In many analytical procedures, the assumption of homogeneity of variances may be false. For example, the precision obtained in spectrophotometry may be limited by the measurement readout error, detector shot noise, or source flicker noise [9]. The classical approach to estimating measurement precision has assumed that the readout error of a linear transmittance scale is the dominant factor; in modern instruments it is far more likely that the dominant factor will be the photomultiplier shot noise.

Agterdenbos [6] has suggested that chemists give more care to the proper selection of the calibration relationship being used when performing a least squares analysis. One method for obtaining the calibration line when the precision of the response measurement is dependent on the analyte concentration is to use a weighted least squares procedure. Weighted least squares regression is analogous to ordinary least squares. Both methods are based on minimizing the sum of the squared deviations between the actual responses and the calibration line. However, when weighted least squares is used, each residual is multiplied by a weighting factor, w_i, proportional to the reciprocal of the variance of the corresponding response measurement, r_i. The relationship to be minimized is now given as

$$\overline{D^2} = \sum_{i=1}^{N} w_i(r_i - \beta_0 c_i - \beta_1)^2 \tag{5}$$

Schwartz [10] has illustrated the potential for nonuniform variance in both spectroscopic and chromatographic experiments. He concluded that if the analyst ignores variance nonuniformity, roughly the same calibration curve will be obtained. However, the confidence bands around the estimated analyte concentration may be severely in error at the extremes of the calibration curve. Garden and co-workers [11] have shown how weighted least squares procedures can improve the precision of the estimated analyte concentration when compared to ordinary least squares calibration.

Deterministic Error

In addition to the statistical errors which may arise from the improper application of least squares methods, the single-component linear model may also be affected by various types of deterministic errors. In most cases these deterministic errors can be traced to violation of the initial assumptions underlying the original model. Often if the source of the error can be identified, the calibration model can be adjusted to bring into consideration the effects of these additional factors.

One serious problem which occurs frequently in analytical chemistry is the presence of a sample matrix effect. This can be defined as a difference in the sensitivity coefficient, k, between the unknown sample being analyzed and the calibration standards. The interaction of the analyte with the sample matrix results in a change in the slope of the calibration plot.

The method of standard addition is widely used in analytical chemistry to address this particular type of problem. The response of the unknown sample is measured, a known amount of the pure analyte is added to the sample, and then the response of the sample after this addition is measured. The initial response measurement, r_0, depends only on the unknown concentration, c_0. After the addition is made the response is a function of both the original analyte present and the amount added. The matrix-corrected sensitivity coefficient is obtained from the change in the response due to the addition of pure analyte. This method still requires the response to be linearly related to the concentration and the sensor to be totally specific for the analyte of interest.

Different groups of workers have applied statistical techniques to calculate the optimum method of making the additions and the resulting precision in the estimate of the analyte concentration [12,13]. The optimal size of the addition to be made is a function of the precision of the sensor and the form of the calibration function. Franke, de Zeeuw, and Hakkert [14] concluded that if a single addition is made, then optimum precision is obtained by making an addition of the largest possible amount of standard without exceeding the linear range of the calibration curve and making an equal number of replicate measurements before and after the addition.

The single-component linear model assumes that the analytical sensor possesses total specificity for the analyte of interest. Implicit in this assumption is a requirement that the response of the sensor at zero analyte concentration is zero response units, or simply stated, the sensor can be zeroed. Two types of problems may lead to failure of this assumption: first, an instrumental or constant background; and second, a sample- or volume-dependent background.

An instrumental background will result in the addition of a constant nonvolume-dependent term, d, to the simple linear model.

$$r = kc + d \qquad (6)$$

In a spectrophotometric analysis, this constant term may arise from the use of mismatched optical paths or cells, temperature differences between the sample and calibration solutions, amplifier offsets, or similar problems. An instrumental background will cause a bias in the concentration estimate obtained from either a normal calibration or a standard addition experiment. Fortunately, this type of background can be handled by standard dilution.

A significantly more difficult problem is the presence of a sample background. In this situation the sensor no longer possesses complete specificity, but responds both to the analyte of interest and also one or more other components present in the sample. This problem has given rise to a multitude of separation and purification techniques directed at eliminating potential interferences. If the identities of the additional components are known and standards of these components are available, then the situation can be treated as a multicomponent analysis problem. However, if the identities of any of the interferents are not known or if calibration with these components is not possible, then the situation represents a sample- or volume-dependent background problem.

Multi-Component Linear Model

The multicomponent linear model is simply a generalization of the familiar single-component model. The responses due to each of the components present in the sample are assumed to add linearly, or can be transformed to yield the total response for any analytical sensor. For the case of two sensors, which respond to both of two analytes, a system of two equations is obtained. This can be written as

$$r_1 = \sum_{i=1}^{2} c_i k_{i1} = c_1 k_{11} + c_2 k_{21}$$

$$r_2 = \sum_{i=1}^{2} c_i k_{i2} = c_1 k_{12} + c_2 k_{22}$$

(7)

where

r_j = response measured at the jth sensor,

c_i = concentration of the ith analyte, and

$k_{i,j}$ = sensitivity coefficient of the jth sensor for the ith analyte.

Each equation represents the measured response for a single analytical sensor as the sum of the responses due to the individual components. For a mixture of N-components, this model is generally written in matrix form as follows

$$r' = c'\mathbf{K}$$

(8)

The vector r is a column vector containing the response of the sample measured with P different sensors. The vector c is a column vector containing the concentrations of the N analytes present in the sample. The prime denotes the transpose of a matrix or vector. The matrix $\mathbf{K}$ contains the sensitivity coefficients for the N-components at each of the P analytical sensors. Each row of the $\mathbf{K}$-matrix contains the P sensitivity coefficients of a single analyte. Each column of the $\mathbf{K}$-matrix contains the sensitivity coefficients of all N-components for the same analytical sensor.

Several assumptions are implicitly made when the multicomponent linear model is used. These assumptions are analogous to the assumptions made with the single-component linear model. First, the response of each sensor is assumed to be linearly related to all analyte concentrations over the concentration ranges of interest. Second, the response due to each component present in the mixture sample is independent of the other $N - 1$ components. Third, the response of each sensor can be zeroed. Lastly, the sensitivity coefficients do not change between the calibration and quantitation steps.

Classification of Samples

Martens, Spjøtvoll, and Volden (*15*) proposed the classification scheme for multicomponent mixtures shown in Table 1. Mixture samples in which the individual component concentrations are known will be designated as

TABLE 1—*Classification of unconstrained additive mixtures.*

Class	Concentrations	Spectra
1A	known	known
1B	known	unknown
2A	unknown	known
2B	unknown	unknown

class 1 samples; those samples in which the component concentrations are not known will be designated as class 2 samples. Class 1 samples are further grouped into two types. The first group is class 1A. These samples are fully defined, both the individual component concentrations and the pure component sensitivities are known to the analyst. In the second group, class 1B, the individual component concentrations are known but the pure component sensitivities are unknown. If N-components are present in the mixture, then estimation of the individual component sensitivities requires either N pure samples or N mixtures of known composition. This class of samples represents the general problem of multicomponent calibration.

Class 2 samples are also grouped into two types. The first group, class 2A, are samples in which the component concentrations are unknown but the individual pure component sensitivities are known. This type of sample is representative of a multicomponent quantitation problem. The second group, class 2B samples, are mixtures in which neither the individual component concentrations nor their sensitivities are known by the analyst.

Analysis of a single class 2B sample is not possible. However, if a set of class 2B samples are available in which the relative concentrations of the components varies from sample to sample, then the methods appropriate to the multicomponent bilinear model may be used to obtain regions of physically allowable pure component sensitivities and concentrations. An unambiguous solution for the sensitivities and individual component concentrations is not possible unless the analytical chemist can obtain further information about the samples.

Calibration

Several different methods are available for calibration in a multicomponent analysis. Kaiser [16] has grouped calibration methods into three main approaches: (1) σ-calibration, or calibration with synthetic standards; (2) α-calibration, or calibration with analyzed standard samples; and (3) δ-calibration, or calibration by differential additions. Of these three methods, calibration with synthetic standard samples is in Kaiser's view the most fundamental. Given a mixture of N-components whose response can be measured at each of P different analytical sensors, the question arises of selecting the best method for first performing the calibration and then estimating the N analyte concentrations. If samples of the N pure components are available, then the simplest method of obtaining the sensitivity coefficients is to measure the response of each pure compound individually. This method may not be always possible. In some cases the pure substances may be very difficult or expensive to obtain, and purify or the mixture may include analytes which are unstable in purified form. If the pure analytes are not available, but it is possible to obtain a set of pre-analyzed standard samples, then the calibration can be based on comparison to these standard mixtures. Finally, if matrix effects are known to be present, the most appropriate method is to use a standard addition analysis to allow calibration within the sample matrix.

Multicomponent calibration based on the analysis of a set of mixture samples of known analyte concentrations to obtain the calibration relationship is frequently used. If a well characterized set of M mixture samples is obtainable, the sensitivity coefficients can be obtained by ordinary or weighted least squares multiple regression. The normal representation of this problem is as follows

$$\mathbf{R} = \mathbf{CK} \qquad (9)$$

where

$\mathbf{R} = M \times P$ matrix of measured responses for each of the M mixture samples,

$\mathbf{C} = M \times N$ matrix containing the N analyte concentrations for each of the mixtures, and

$\mathbf{K} =$ defined as before.

Since the concentrations of all of the analytes in each mixture sample are known and the mixture responses can be measured, the sensitivity matrix, $\mathbf{K}$, can be obtained by multiplying both sides of Eq 9 by the inverse of C. If there are the same number of mixture samples as analytes present, that is, $M = N$, then this system of linear equations is exactly determined and the calibration step requires inverting C to yield

$$\mathbf{K} = \mathbf{C}^{-1}\mathbf{R} \qquad (10)$$

However, if the number of calibration mixtures used is greater than the number of analytes, that is, $M > N$, then the best estimate of the sensitivity matrix, $\mathbf{K}$, is generally calculated from least squares multiple regression in matrix form. The generalized inverse solution for the sensitivity matrix is given as

$$\mathbf{K} = (\mathbf{C}'\mathbf{C})^{-1}\mathbf{C}'\mathbf{R} \qquad (11)$$

In order to obtain the sensitivity matrix, $\mathbf{K}$, from either Eq 10 or 11, the number of analytical sensors, P, must be greater than or equal to the number of analytes. The analyte concentrations in a unknown mixture sample can be obtained by measuring its response and multiplying the transposed response vector by the generalized inverse of $\mathbf{K}$

$$c' = r'\mathbf{K}(\mathbf{KK}')^{-1} \tag{12}$$

For the entire analysis, calibration and quantitation of N analytes, this procedure requires at least N mixture samples, and inversion of two $N \times N$ matrices; $\mathbf{C}'\mathbf{C}$ and $\mathbf{KK}'$.

Brown and associates [17,18] have proposed an alternative formulation of the matrix multicomponent model, where instead of considering the response as a function of concentration, they consider the concentration a function of the measured response. This is written as

$$\mathbf{C} = \mathbf{RP} \tag{13}$$

where the matrices $\mathbf{C}$ and $\mathbf{R}$ are defined as before and the matrix $\mathbf{P}$ represents the proportionality between $\mathbf{C}$ and $\mathbf{R}$. The matrix $\mathbf{P}$ will have dimensions of $P \times N$, that is, sensors by analytes. For this model, the calibration step is expressed as

$$\mathbf{P} = (\mathbf{R}'\mathbf{R})^{-1}\mathbf{R}'\mathbf{C} \tag{14}$$

which requires the inversion of the $P \times P$ matrix, $\mathbf{R}'\mathbf{R}$. Quantitation of an unknown sample is accomplished directly by multiplying the response vector, r, by the calibration matrix, $\mathbf{P}$, to yield

$$c' = r'\mathbf{P} \tag{15}$$

The authors state that this method has the advantage of requiring only one matrix inversion instead of the two required by the conventional notation. Subsequently, they used this method for the spectrophotometric analysis of serum lipids with 85 calibration samples and 15 analytical wavelengths [19].

The difficulty in this analysis lies in the relative dimensions of the various matrices. In order to obtain a solution of Eq 14 there must be more calibration mixtures than sensors being used. This is a drawback when the availability of diode array spectrophotometers makes it possible to measure 256 or more wavelengths as easily as four or five. In order to use all of the available wavelengths, one calibration sample must be prepared for every sensor used. Additionally, as the number of calibration samples and wavelengths are increased the size of the matrix $\mathbf{R}'\mathbf{R}$, which must be inverted in the calibration step, is also increased. If the sensors themselves are highly correlated or if the number of analytes is much less than the number of sensors, then the matrix $R'R$ may have an effective rank of much less than P. In this situation, $R'R$ will be almost singular and the inversion will be numerically unstable.

The method of principal component regression can be used as an alternative to ordinary least squares multiple regression [20]. This method is based on replacing the $M \times P$ response matrix, R, with the product of two smaller matrices, T and B. Equation 13 can now be written as

$$C = TBP \tag{16}$$

where the matrix T has dimensions $M \times A$ and the matrix B has dimensions $A \times P$, with $A << N$ and $A << P$. Decomposition of R into the matrices T and B is called singular value decomposition, eigenvector projection, factor analysis, or principal component analysis, depending on the scaling of R. The matrices T and B are selected in order to represent R as closely as possible and such that the columns of T and the rows of B are both orthogonal. Geometrically, the decomposition of R into T-B can be considered as a projection of the original data points, or mixture spectra, from a P-dimensional measurement space into a smaller A-dimensional space. The matrix T, whose elements are sometimes called the factor scores, contains the coordinates of the data points in the new A-dimensional space and the matrix B, containing the factor loadings, is the rotation matrix used to perform the projection. Solution of the original calibration problem now requires the inversion of $T'T$ instead of $R'R$. Since the columns of T are orthogonal, this inversion is numerically well conditioned. This yields a calibration matrix G instead of the calibration matrix P.

$$G = BP = (T'T)^{-1}T'C \tag{17}$$

The desired calibration matrix P can then easily be found as

$$P = B'G \tag{18}$$

The quantitation step is exactly the same as used by Brown and co-workers [17,18].

A different approach to the multicomponent calibration problem, called partial least squares (PLS) in latent variables, has been suggested by S. Wold and co-workers [21]. PLS was developed by H. Wold [22] to solve complex data analysis problems in econometrics and psychometrics. It is somewhat analogous to principal component multiple regression in that the independent variables, in this case the matrix R, are described by a principal component type model and then combined with a regression relationship relating the responses to the analyte concentrations contained in the matrix

C. The difference is that in the PLS method the projection **T** is computed not only to model **R** but also to maximize its correlation with **C.** In principal component regression, **T** is selected only to model **R.** The PLS method involves first scaling both the response matrix, **R,** and the concentration matrix, **C,** such that the standard deviation of each column in these matrices is equal to one. The matrices are then centered by subtracting the average for each column. Each matrix is then modeled as a linear combination of new orthogonal latent variables. The latent variables are calculated by an iterative method which does not involve an explicit regression step. The maximum number of latent variables is the actual number of independent variables; however, normally fewer latent variables are used to allow filtering of the noise present in the data set. The PLS model is described as follows

$$c_{ij} = \bar{c}_j + \sum_{l=1}^{A} u_{il}b_{lj} + \epsilon'_{ij} \tag{19}$$

$$r_{ik} = \bar{r}_k + \sum_{l=1}^{A} t_{il}d_{lk} + \epsilon''_{ik} \tag{20}$$

$$u_{il} = \rho_l t_{il} \quad \text{for all } l = 1, \ldots A \tag{21}$$

where

$u_{i,l}$ and $t_{i,l}$ are the latent variables and
$b_{i,j}$ and $d_{i,k}$ are the loadings used to describe the concentration and response matrices, respectively.

Equations 19 and 20, known as the outer relationship, describe the projection of the original variables into an A-dimensional space. Equation 21, known as the inner relationship, describes the correlation between the latent variables. The quantitation step in PLS is accomplished by first centering and scaling the measured response spectrum of an unknown mixture, calculating the latent variables, $t_{i,l}$, from the loadings, $b_{i,j}$, calculating the latent variables, $u_{i,l}$, from the inner relationship, and then estimating the concentrations from Eq 19. The PLS method has been compared to principal component regression for the multicomponent calibration and quantitation of spectrofluorimetric data from mixtures of humic acid and ligninsulfonate by Lindberg and co-workers [23]. They concluded that: first, PLS was computationally faster than principal component regression; second, PLS calibrations have better predictive qualities since the method extracts information which has predictive relevance for the concentrations of the calibration mixture; third, a criterion could be established for determining if the calibration model was appropriate for a given unknown mixture; and fourth, like other methods based on principal component analysis, PLS was able to compensate for unidentified fluorescent species in the solution. This final conclusion implies that an analyte can be quantitated in the presence of a totally unknown background, but the experimental data reported does not support this conclusion.

It was already noted that matrix effects can affect the accuracy of the calibration in a single component analysis. Exactly the same difficulties may arise with the multicomponent linear model. As Kaiser [16] noted, standard additions provide the most appropriate calibration method if matrix effects occur. When discussing the single component linear model, it was observed that in most cases, the well-known standard addition method was able to correct for these matrix effects, but the simple standard addition method required a fully selective sensor. Saxberg and Kowalski [24] have developed a multicomponent extension of the standard addition method which they named the generalized standard addition method or GSAM. The generalized standard addition method has two distinct advantages: first, it allows the use of nonselective analytical sensors; and second, it corrects for the presence of matrix effects. The first advantage is a byproduct of the multicomponent nature of the method. This does not require the individual sensors to be fully selective for any one analyte; however, it does require that the sensors do not respond to components in the sample of which additions have not been made. The second advantage is the result of using standard additions and making all the measurements within the sample matrix in order to obtain the sensitivity matrix, $\mathbf{K}$. The response of each sensor is normally assumed to obey the linear multicomponent model given in Eq 8, but models involving higher dimension polynomial relationships between the concentration and absorbance were described.

Experimentally, GSAM requires that M additions are made to the sample being analyzed. Each addition may contain one or more of the pure analytes; however, the additions must be made such that each pure analyte is added to the sample at least once. After each addition the response at each of P analytical sensors is measured. The response after the mth addition is modeled as

$$r'_m = c'_m \mathbf{K} \tag{22}$$

where

r_m = a column vector containing the measured responses, and
c_m = a column vector containing the total concentrations of analyte present $(c_0 + \Delta c)$.

The response matrix, $\mathbf{R}$, and the concentration matrix, $\mathbf{C}$, are defined as

$$\mathbf{R}' = [r_1, r_2, r_3, \ldots r_{\mathbf{M}}] \tag{23}$$

$$\mathbf{C}' = [c_1, c_2, c_3, \ldots c_{\mathbf{M}}] \tag{24}$$

This allows a simple formulation of the problem as

$$\mathbf{R} = \mathbf{CK} \tag{25}$$

Each row of $\mathbf{R}$ and $\mathbf{C}$ corresponds to a separate multiple standard addition. The matrix $\mathbf{R}$ is always known. The matrix $\mathbf{C}$ is unknown since each row includes the unknown analyte concentration plus the amount of analyte which has been added. The matrix of sensitivity coefficients, $\mathbf{K}$, is also unknown. Solution of this linear multiple linear system is accomplished by separating the terms as follows

$$\mathbf{C} = \Delta\mathbf{C} + \mathbf{C}_0 \tag{26}$$

$$\mathbf{R} = \Delta\mathbf{R} + \mathbf{R}_0 \tag{27}$$

where $\mathbf{C}_0$ and $\mathbf{R}_0$ are matrices with all rows identical to the initial concentration and initial response vectors c_0 and r_0, respectively, and $\Delta\mathbf{C}$ and $\Delta\mathbf{R}$ are the matrices of the net change in concentrations and responses due to the standard additions. $\Delta\mathbf{C}$ and $\Delta\mathbf{R}$ are always known to the analyst; hence, the sensitivity coefficients can be calculated from

$$\Delta\mathbf{R} = \Delta\mathbf{CK} \tag{28}$$

The calibration step in GSAM is equivalent to the solution of this linear system. Assuming $N \neq M$, the solution is found by

$$\mathbf{K} = (\Delta\mathbf{C}'\Delta\mathbf{C})^{-1}\Delta\mathbf{C}'\Delta\mathbf{R} \tag{29}$$

or if $N = M$, then $\Delta\mathbf{C}$ can be inverted directly. The quantitation step is given by Eq 12. This is identical to the earlier discussion of the least squares matrix solution of the multicomponent model. It must be also noted that the matrix $\Delta\mathbf{C}$ contains the effective concentration changes after each standard addition. Unless the volume changes are negligible, $\Delta\mathbf{C}$ cannot be known since the initial concentrations are not known. This problem can be avoided by incorporating a simple volume correction into the GSAM to convert from analyte concentrations to absolute quantities. Equation 22 is now written as

$$r'_m = (1/V_m)n'_m\mathbf{K} \tag{30}$$

where the vector n_m contains the absolute quantities, in grams or moles, of each analyte in a volume, V_m. Multiplying both sides of this equation by V_m leads to

$$q'_m = V_m r'_m = n'_m\mathbf{K} \tag{31}$$

where the vector q_m contains the P volume corrected responses. The remaining equations are obtained by substituting the volume corrected responses; q, $\mathbf{Q}$, and $\Delta\mathbf{Q}$, for the responses; r, $\mathbf{R}$, and $\Delta\mathbf{R}$, and by substituting the absolute quantities; n, $\mathbf{N}$, and $\Delta\mathbf{N}$, for the concentrations; c, $\mathbf{C}$, and $\Delta\mathbf{C}$.

Several more recent papers have examined the error propagation and statistical aspects of using the GSAM. Jochum, Jochum, and Kowalski [25] have stated the accuracy of GSAM in obtaining valid estimates of the initial analyte concentrations is dependent on at least five distinct factors: first, the accuracy of the response measurements; second, the accuracy and precision of the multiple standard additions; third, the magnitude of the interanalyte response interferences; fourth, the experimental design; and finally, the mathematical algorithms used in the computations. The first two of these factors are no different than the considerations required for any analytical method. The final factor, selection of the mathematical algorithms, can affect the results by introducing round-off errors into the computations. The upper bound on relative errors in the estimated concentrations was found to depend on the condition number of both the calibration matrix, $\mathbf{K}$, and the experimental design, which is described by the addition matrix, $\Delta\mathbf{N}$. The condition number of any nonsingular matrix $\mathbf{A}$ is defined as

$$\text{cond}(\mathbf{A}) = \|\mathbf{A}\| \, \|\mathbf{A}^{-1}\| \tag{32}$$

where $\|\mathbf{A}\|$ is the Euclidian norm of the matrix $\mathbf{A}$. If the matrix $\mathbf{A}$ is rectangular, then its condition number is given as

$$\text{cond}(\mathbf{A}) = [\text{cond}(\mathbf{A}'\mathbf{A})]^{1/2} \tag{33}$$

It is important to note that the condition number of any matrix is always equal to or greater than one. In the GSAM experiment, the $\mathbf{K}$-matrix is determined by the solution of an overdetermined system of linear equations, and, therefore, this matrix is not exactly known. Jochum, Jochum, and Kowalski showed that errors in the response measurements can be amplified by the chemist's choice of experimental design. An estimate of the error in the calculated $\mathbf{K}$-matrix was found to be

$$\frac{\|\bar{k} - k\|}{\|k\|} \leq \text{cond}(\Delta\mathbf{N}) \, \frac{\|\overline{\Delta q_1} - \Delta q_1\|}{\|\Delta q_1\|} \tag{34}$$

where Δq_1 and $\overline{\Delta q}_1$ are the projections of Δq and $\Delta\bar{q}$ onto the range of $\mathbf{N}$. A modification of the computational algorithm, called the incremental difference calculation, was described which minimized the error amplification due to the experimental design. In the incremental difference calculation the $\Delta\mathbf{Q}$-matrix is composed of the change in volume corrected response between two successive additions and the ΔN-matrix is composed of the absolute quantity of analyte added in a single addition. After scaling the condition number of the ΔN-matrix is equal to one, which results in no error amplification being introduced in the final concentration estimates due to the experimental design.

The condition number of the K-matrix can also lead to a magnification of the potential concentration errors. The authors showed that, in the worst case, a small relative error in the initial response vector, r_0, could be magnified by the cond(K) to produce a larger relative concentration error. The error in the concentration estimates was found to be

$$\frac{\|\delta c_0\|}{\|c_0\|} \leq \text{cond}(K) \left[\frac{\|\delta r_0\|}{\|r_0\|} + \frac{\|\delta k\|}{\|k\|} \right] \tag{35}$$

where δc_0, δr_0, and δk are the errors present in c_0, r_0, and K, respectively. Recently, Kalivas [26] showed the condition number of the K-matrix is a extremely useful tool for assessing the analytical cost in terms of relative uncertainty of varying sensor selectivity. Minimization of the condition number of the K-matrix can be used as a criteria for the selection of the optimal set of sensors for a particular multicomponent analysis.

Moran and Kowalski [27] have considered the statistical aspects of the GSAM. They have found that the uncertainty in the estimates of the sensitivity coefficients, that is, the $k_{i,j}$'s, is dependent on three terms; the measurement variance, correlation of the response measurements due to subtraction of the initial response, and variance arising from the volume increase as a result of making standard additions. In order to reduce the variance and obtain the best possible accuracy in the concentration estimates, they recommend several steps. First, the volume increases must be minimized. Second, if random noise is the dominant source of error, then the total difference calculation method should be used. Third, the largest possible additions of analyte should be made.

Quantitation

Presuming the sensitivity matrix, K, has been obtained, the quantitation step can be approached by an extension of the single component model. Sternberg, Stillo, and Schwendeman [28] have described the application of the least squares method in matrix form to the spectrophotometric analysis of a five component mixture. They noted certain restrictions are necessary to assure a solution to the matrix problem will exist. The length of the response vector, r, and the column dimension of the sensitivity matrix, K, must be equal to or greater than the number of analytes; therefore, P must be greater than or equal to N. In addition the rank of the sensitivity matrix must be at least N, which implies the P sensors must span a minimum of an N-dimensional space. If there are exactly the same number of sensors as there are analytes present, that is, $N = P$, then the solution to the matrix problem is simply given as

$$c' = r' \, \mathbf{K}^{-1} \qquad (36)$$

However, if more sensors than the minimum number necessary to obtain a solution to the system of linear equations are used, that is, $P > N$, then the method of least squares can be used to obtain the set of estimated analyte concentrations which minimizes the difference between the measured responses and the responses predicted by the multicomponent linear model. The solution to this least squares problem in matrix form was given in Eq 12. Two years later, Zscheile and co-workers [29] used the matrix form of the least squares method to examine a four component spectrophotometric system. In analyzing a system of RNA-constitutents, they observed the stability of the concentration estimates was very dependent on the wavelengths selected for the analysis. The poor stability obtained with some sets of wavelengths was attributed to linear dependence of the underlying pure analyte spectra. The best results were obtained when all the available wavelengths were used.

The same considerations regarding homogeneity of variance, which were necessary for the single component linear model, must be also made when the multicomponent model is used. Haaland and Easterling [30] applied a linear additive multicomponent model to the analysis of infrared spectra of xylene isomer mixtures. They observed the noise characteristics of most infrared detectors were such that the noise was generally constant and independent of the signal level. The signal measured by these detectors is in transmittance, which is then converted to absorbance. Since Beer's law is generally obeyed in this spectral region the absorbance is directly proportional to concentration; however, the precision of the absorbance measurements are not independent of the measured responses. To account for this nonhomogeneity, Haaland and Easterling used a weighted least squares procedure. Expanding the absorbance signal as a Taylor series about the transmittance and retaining only the first two terms, they found the variance of the noise was proportional to the inverse of the square of the transmittance. Therefore, they performed the analysis by first weighting each measured response in the spectrum by a factor equal to its transmittance squared. The matrix form of the weighted least squares estimate of the analyte concentrations is given by

$$c' = r'\mathbf{V}^{-1}\mathbf{K}'(\mathbf{KVK}')^{-1} \qquad (37)$$

where the matrix $\mathbf{V}$ is a diagonal matrix containing the reciprocal of the weights. This method of weighting assumes the errors in the responses are independent but with different variances. If the response measurements are correlated, Eq 37 may still be used; however, the matrix $\mathbf{V}$ is no longer diagonal [4].

Deterministic Errors

As was observed with the single component model, various types of deterministic errors may affect the multicomponent linear model. These errors, which may be due to chemical, for example, matrix effects or interferences, or instrumental factors, for example, drifting or nonzeroed sensors, result in violating the assumptions present in the linear additive response model. In two recent papers [31,32], Kalivas and Kowalski have extended the GSAM model to add one or more terms to the basic model which allow for the detection and correction of sensor drift occurring during the course of the analysis. The GSAM model with the inclusion of terms for so-called time additions is

$$r_{ml} = \sum_{j=1}^{N} c_{mj} k_{jl} + \sum_{i=1}^{W} t^i k_{N+1,l} \tag{38}$$

where W is the polynomial order of the drift model. Volume correction was performed as earlier described. The $N + 1^{st}$ to W^{th} rows of the $\mathbf{K}$-matrix represent the coefficients of the drift model. The drift coefficients can be examined statistically in order to detect the presence of a drifting analytical sensor. Estimation of the initial analyte quantities is accomplished as before, after deletion from the $\mathbf{K}$-matrix of the rows containing the sensitivity coefficients for the time additions. Implementation of the drift correcting GSAM model requires augmenting the $\Delta\mathbf{N}$-matrix with W-rows containing the time elapsed since the initial response measurement raised to the appropriate power. This was accomplished by developing a completely automated system for making the standard additions, measuring the responses, and recording the elapsed time [32]. In addition to implementing the time additions and drift correction, this system was designed to make the standard additions by weight instead of by volume in order to minimize the relative errors in measuring the amount of analyte added.

Implicit in the multicomponent linear model is an assumption that the response of the analytical sensors can be zeroed. Two types of model failure have been identified in connection with this assumption: first, an instrumental or constant background; and second, a sample or volume dependent background. Altering the multicomponent model to compensate for an instrumental background can be accomplished by adding a constant term for each sensor

$$r' = c'\mathbf{K} + d' \tag{39}$$

where the vector d contains the background contribution at each of the $\mathbf{P}$ analytical sensors. Vandeginste, Klaessens, and Kateman [33] have shown a dilution procedure can be used to correct for a constant background response. Equation 39 is rewritten for volume corrected responses as

$$V_0 r_0' = V_0(c_0'\mathbf{K} + d) = n_0'\mathbf{K} + V_0 d' \tag{40}$$

where

V_0 = initial volume of the sample mixture,
r_0 = initial response vector,
c_0 = initial concentration vector, and
n_0 = vector of initial analyte quantities.

A standard dilution is performed by adding a volume, Δv, of pure solvent to the mixture sample. Equation 39 can again be rewritten in terms of the volume corrected responses; however, now the total sample volume is $V_0 + \Delta v$. Since the absolute quantities of analyte present have not been affected by the dilution, the difference in the volume corrected responses, Δq, is simply

$$\Delta q' = q' - q_0' = \Delta v d' \tag{41}$$

This relationship allows estimation of the constant background vector, d, since it is a function of only the added volume, Δv, and the vector of measured changes in the volume corrected responses, Δq.

The presence of additional components in the sample mixture gives rise to a sample or volume dependent background. This can be incorporated into the standard multicomponent linear model by adding additional terms which express the response as a function of the known analytes and the additional interferents. The expanded model is

$$r_l = \sum_{i=1}^{N} c_i k_{il} + \sum_{j=1}^{T} c_j k_{jl} \quad \text{for all } l = 1, \ldots P \tag{42}$$

where r_l is the response of the lth sensor. The first summation, which runs from one to N, accounts for the response caused by the N known analytes. The second summation, which runs from one to T, accounts for the response caused by the presence of the T interfering components. Since the identities of the T interfering components are not known, no standards for these components can be used nor can standard additions of these components be made. Hence, during the course of the analysis, the relative amounts of the interferents with respect to each other will not change. Therefore, these

T interferents can be replaced by a single term which represents their combined influence on the measured sensor responses

$$r_l = \sum_{i=1}^{N} c_i k_{il} + f_l \quad \text{for all } i = 1, \ldots P \qquad (43)$$

where f_l is the combined background response at sensor l. The important distinction between this model and the model, given in Eq 39 which describes an instrumental background, is that the term f_l is a function of the sample volume; therefore, the standard dilution method used by Vandeginste does not apply. Since the sample background, f_l, is not known, an exact solution does not exist and an iterative method must be used to perform mixture quantitation.

In their original paper describing the GSAM model, Saxberg and Kowalski [24] discussed the problem of analytical sensors which were not zeroed. They observed that if the background response was small relative to the initial unknown response and the problem was reasonably insensitive to perturbations, then the effect on the final solution can be expected to be small. Leggett [34] has applied nonnegative least squares regression and simplex optimization to multicomponent spectrophotometric data. He concluded either of these methods avoid the problem of negative molar absorptivities or concentrations which are sometimes obtained when ordinary least squares regression has been used. This conclusion was reached with the stated assumption that the correct model, for example, all components were known, had been used to set up the analysis. Gayle and Bennett [35] carried out simulation studies to determine the effect of model departure in multicomponent analysis on the concentration estimates obtained by ordinary least squares regression, nonnegative least squares regression, and linear programming. They observed that when various types of model failure were simulated, all three methods yielded biased results, with no single method being consistently superior to the other two. In addition, of the three methods attempted only ordinary least squares provided any indication that the model was not valid. Omission of significant terms in this model frequently led to negative analyte concentrations, a result which obviously had no chemical meaning. However, nonnegative least squares regression and linear programming yielded results which at least on the surface seemed chemically plausible, but were also significantly in error.

The final type of model failure which may occur is a failure of the assumed linear relationship between analyte concentration and the measured response. Apparent deviations from the ideal behavior described by the Beer-Lambert law, which is widely used in spectrophotometric analysis, are well known. Saxberg and Kowalski [24] developed the original GSAM model to allow the response to be either a linear, quadratic, or higher degree polynomial function of the analyte concentration. Unfortunately, as the number of terms in the model increases, so does the required number of standard additions and measurements which the analyst must make. An alternative approach has been used by Vandeginste and co-workers [33] involving the application of a mathematical technique known as Kalman filtering to provide continuous testing of the validity of the linear model during the data acquisition stage of a GSAM experiment. Poulisse [36] has also applied the Kalman filter to the analysis of multicomponent spectrophotometric mixtures. Seelig and Blount [37,38] have applied this method to anodic stripping voltammetry, and S. Brown and co-workers [39,40] have used the Kalman filter with linear sweep voltammetry and photoacoustic spectroscopy. This filter relies on a recursive algorithim which constantly updates the estimated sensitivities as more standard mixtures are analyzed. The recursive nature of this filter, which has only recently seen application in analytical chemistry, has the potential of providing feedback for on line evaluation and optimization of the calibration process.

Multicomponent Bilinear Models

The multicomponent bilinear model is obtained when a second measurement dimension is incorporated into the multicomponent linear model. This model describes the response of a single mixture sample along two independent measurement axes. Important applications of the bilinear model in analytical chemistry include instrumental techniques based on two spectroscopic measurements, for example, fluorescence emission-excitation matrices (EEMs), and techniques based on a combination of chromatographic and spectroscopic measurements, for example, LC/UV, GC/MS, or GC/FT-IR analyses. The response of a single component can be described as

$$\mathbf{M} = \alpha x y' \tag{44}$$

where $\mathbf{M}$ contains the measured responses and is the outer product of the vectors x and y multiplied by a concentration dependent factor, α. The vector x represents the spectral, chromatographic, or temporal profile in the first dimension and y represents the spectral, chromatographic, or temporal profile of the compound in the second dimension. For example, a GC/MS peak consisting of 50 mass spectra each composed of 20 distinct m/e ratios would result in a matrix of spectral intensities, $\mathbf{M}$, containing 50 rows and 20 columns. The vector x would have 50 elements and describe the gas chromatographic elution profile. The vector y would have 20 elements and represent the mass spectrum of the pure compound. Normally, x and y are normalized to a length of one, so that the factor α is then proportional to the standard concentration of the pure compound. Assuming that each component in a **N**-component mixture responds independently of the remaining **N** $-$ 1 components, the response of the mixture can be represented by

$$\mathbf{M} = \sum_{i=1}^{N} c_i \mathbf{M}_i = \sum_{i=1}^{N} c_i (\alpha x y')_i \qquad (45)$$

where

$\mathbf{M}_i$ = response matrix due to component i at its standard concentration in the mixture, and

c_i = concentration of the ith component divided by its standard or unit concentration.

Least Squares Multiple Regression

The analysis of the data obtained from an experimental system, which is described by the multicomponent bilinear model, depends on the information available to the analyst. A common problem is the quantitation of several components whose identities are known and whose standard matrices are available. In this situation, least squares regression may be used. The objective is to minimize the sum of the squared elements of the residual matrix, **E,** which is defined as

$$\mathbf{E}_{ij} = \mathbf{M}_{ij} - \sum_{k=1}^{N} \beta_k (\mathbf{M}_{ij})_k \qquad (46)$$

where the parameters β_k are the amounts of each of the k-compounds present in the mixture. Warner, Davidson, and Christian [41] have applied this method to the analysis of fluorescence emission-excitation matrices. The least squares approach, while easy to implement and conceptually simple, yields accurate results only if standards of all of the mixture components are included in the data analysis.

Rank Annihilation

In many situations, the identities of all components contributing to the measured response may not be known. Ho and co-workers [42,43] have developed the method of rank annihilation to allow the quantitation of one or several components without requiring knowledge of all of the components in a mixture sample. They have applied this method to the quantitative analysis of multicomponent emission-excitation matrices (EEMs) obtained from the analysis of polynuclear aromatic hydrocarbon mixtures with the video fluorometer. Ideally the mixture matrix, **M,** should have a rank equal to the number of components, *N*, in the mixture. For a mixture of *N*-components, the best least squares approximation of **M** is given by

$$\hat{\mathbf{M}} = \sum_{k=1}^{N} \xi_k u_k v_k'$$ (47)

where

$$\mathbf{M}v_k = \xi_k u_k$$ (48)

and

$$\mathbf{M}'u_k = \xi_k v_k$$ (49)

The eigenvectors $\{u_1, \ldots u_N\}$ and $\{v_1, \ldots v_N\}$ should span the same vector spaces as the pure component vectors $\{x_1, \ldots x_N\}$ and $\{y_1, \ldots y_N\}$. The number of nonzero eigenvalues, ξ_k, equals the number of components in the sample. In order to perform rank annihilation an amount, β, of the standard matrix, $\mathbf{M}_1$, which corresponds to a component known to be present in the mixture, is subtracted from the mixture matrix, **M,** to yield

$$\mathbf{E} = \mathbf{M} - \beta\mathbf{M}_1$$ (50)

When the correct value of β, corresponding to the concentration of $\mathbf{M}_1$ in **M,** has been subtracted the rank of $\mathbf{EE}'$ will be $N - 1$. This is indicated by one of the nonzero eigenvalues in $\mathbf{EE}'$ approaching zero. Since real data contains experimental error, the eigenvalue does not become exactly zero, but it does have a distinct minimum. The advantages of this technique are that it does not require the knowledge of all of the sample constituents or the presence of selective spectral regions.

If quantitation of several known species in a multicomponent bilinear mixture are desired, then an extension of rank annihilation based on the Fletcher-Powell algorithm may be used [*44*]. This algorithm allows simultaneous computation of the concentrations of all known components in the mixture sample. McCue and Malinowski [*45*] have used rank annihilation of UV absorbance spectra to quantify coeluting liquid chromatographic peaks. Applying rank annihilation to LC/UV data requires that the elution profiles of each individual component in the mixture are exactly reproducible between the chromatographed standard samples and the mixture.

Self Modeling Curve Resolution

In 1971, Lawton and Sylvester [46] reported a method, which they called self modeling curve resolution, for resolving two unknown overlapping functions from an observed set of mixtures of the two functions. They noted that this type of problem arises frequently in areas such as chromatography and spectrophotometry. This method is based on the assumption that neither the identities of the individual components nor their responses are known, but the responses for a number of mixtures of varying relative amounts of the same underlying components have been measured. The objectives of self modeling curve resolution are twofold: first, to estimate the spectra of the underlying pure components; and second to quantify the amount of each pure component present in a given mixture. The model developed by Lawton and Sylvester can be described as follows. The measured response of a mixture of two pure components can be expressed as the sum of the responses of the individual components. This is simply the two component case of the multicomponent linear model developed in the last section and can be written

$$m = x_1 y_1 + x_2 y_2 \tag{51}$$

where m represents a single mixture spectrum, x_1 and x_2 are the concentrations of the two pure components, and the vectors y_1 and y_2 are the spectra of the pure components. Normalization of the pure component spectra does not restrict the shape of the unknown spectra. The concentrations x_1 and x_2 are now defined relative to the concentration of analyte which produces an absorbance spectrum of unit area. If N different mixture samples of these two components are measured, then the entire data set can be expressed in matrix form as

$$\mathbf{M} = \mathbf{XY} \tag{52}$$

where

$\mathbf{M}$ = a $N \times P$ matrix of measured responses,
$\mathbf{X}$ = a $N \times 2$ matrix of analyte concentrations, and
$\mathbf{Y}$ = a $2 \times P$ matrix of analyte spectra scaled to unit area.

Since only two components are present, each observed mixture spectrum, for example, each row of $\mathbf{M}$, can be expressed as a linear combination of the first two eigenvectors of the second moment matrix, $\mathbf{M'M}/N$. That is

$$m_i = \epsilon_{i1} V_1 + \epsilon_{i2} V_2 \tag{53}$$

where

$$m_i = \text{the } i^{\text{th}} \text{ mixture spectrum, and}$$
$$V_1 \text{ and } V_2 = \text{the eigenvectors associated with the two largest eigenvalues}$$
$$\text{of } \mathbf{M'M}/N$$

The spectra, y_1 and y_2, of the two pure components must be also linear combinations of these two eigenvectors.

$$y_i = \eta_{i1}V_1 + \eta_{i2}V_2 \qquad \text{for } i = 1,2 \tag{54}$$

Determination of the values of η_{i1} and η_{i2} is equivalent to estimation of the unknown pure spectra.

Lawton and Sylvester applied three restrictions in order to obtain physically meaningful estimates of the pure spectra, y_1 and y_2. The first restriction was that all elements of the unknown pure spectra must be nonnegative. This implies that η_{i1} and η_{i2} must satisfy

$$\eta_{i1}v_{1k} + \eta_{i2}v_{2k} \geq 0 \qquad \text{for all } k = 1, \ldots P \tag{55}$$

where v_{jk} is the kth element of eigenvector V_j. This is equivalent in a chemical sense to not allowing negative absorbances. The second restriction was that all of the mixture spectra must be composed of nonnegative amounts of the two pure components. This requires $x_{ij} > 0$ for all i and j. From Eqs 52, 54, and 55, it can be shown this restriction is equivalent to requiring $x_{i1} > 0$ and $x_{i2} > 0$ in

$$(\epsilon_{i1}, \epsilon_{i2}) = x_{i1}(\eta_{11}, \eta_{12}) + x_{i2}(\eta_{21}, \eta_{22}) \qquad \text{for all } i = 1, \ldots S \tag{56}$$

The final restriction was based on the assumption that the unknown spectra, y_i, have been normalized to unit area. Figure 1 illustrates these three restrictions plotted in the 2-dimensional eigenvector space $\{V_1, V_2\}$. The angle formed by the inner constraint in Fig. 1 represents the range of relative analyte concentrations within the set of mixture samples. The angle formed by the outer constraint is related to the spectral uniqueness of the two pure components. Without requiring any assumptions as to the shape of the spectral curves, two regions, F_I and F_{II}, which contain the eigenvector representation of the pure spectra, y_1 and y_2, were obtained.

Sharaf and Kowalski [47, 48] have considered the problem of quantitation in the two dimensional eigenvector space. They have shown that quantitative resolution of the two components in any given mixture spectrum is a straight forward function of the relative positions of the two pure spectra and the mixture spectrum in the eigenvector space. Assuming the mixture spectrum

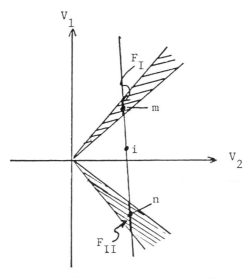

FIG. 1—*Generalized plot of two dimensional eigenvector space. The outer edges of the shaded region represent the non-negative response constraint. The inner edges represent the non-negative quantity constraint. The regions* F_I *and* F_{II} *are the allowable regions for the location of the pure spectra* m *and* n.

has been normalized to unit area, it will fall somewhere along the line segment separating regions F_I and F_{II} in Fig. 1. In order to quantify as a mixture spectrum, the positions of the pure spectra, y_1 and y_2 within the regions F_I and F_{II}, respectively, must be known or estimated. If point m in region F_I is selected to represent the pure spectrum of component 1 and point n in region F_{II} is selected to represent the pure spectrum of component 2: then Sharaf and Kowalski proved the fraction of the total response of mixture i due to component 1, F_{i1}, is given by

$$F_{i1} = d_{ni}/d_{mn} \qquad (57)$$

where

d_{ni} = euclidean distance from point n to mixture i, and
d_{mn} = distance from point m in region F_I to point n in region F_{II}.

The analogous expression for the fraction of the total response of mixture is due to component 2, F_{i2}, is given as

$$F_{i2} = d_{mi}/d_{mn} \qquad (58)$$

The major problem to be addressed in quantitating mixture spectra is the selection of the points m and n to be used as the best estimates of the pure spectra, y_1 and y_2. Sharaf and Kowalski considered several possibilities. First, if the width of the solution bands, F_I and F_{II}, are equal to zero, then pure spectra of both components have been measured and at least one specific sensor (for example, wavelength, mass/charge ratio) exists for each component. In this case no assumptions are necessary to correctly quantify the mixture spectra. Second, if the solution bandwidths are not zero but specific sensors are known to exist, then all measured samples are mixtures of both components. Since specific sensors are known, the outer edges of the solution bands are the correct choice for the estimates of the pure component spectra. Third, if the solution bandwidths are not zero and specific sensors are not known to exist, then some assumptions must be made in order to quantify the mixture. The authors recommended using the inner edges of the solution bands, for example the purest spectra recorded, as an initial estimate of the pure component spectra. Alternately, the midpoints of each region may be used in the absence of further information.

A similar approach to curve resolution has been used by Martens [49]. The major difference in the model used by Martens compared to that used by Lawton and Sylvester is that prior to extracting the eigenvectors of the moment matrix, Martens normalized the mixture spectra to constant area and centered the data matrix by subtracting the mean response of each sensor. This resulted in one fewer eigenvector being required to represent the mixture spectra in the reduced eigenvector space. Therefore, a mixture spectrum containing two underlying components can be represented by a linear combination of the mean and the first eigenvector of the centered covariance matrix. The advantage of this additional step is twofold: first, one fewer dimension is necessary to represent the data; hence, the factor analysis solution is somewhat easier to interpret, and second, the large trival variance associated with the mean has been removed by centering the data. Martens has made the same assumptions as were used by Lawton and Sylvester: first, only nonnegative responses are allowed; second, only nonnegative quantities of analytes may be present; and third, the pure component spectra are scaled to constant area. Spjøtvoll, Martens, and Volden [15] have compared the constraint equations for the two dimensional case using the mean plus one eigenvector model to the constraint equations as formulated by Lawton and Sylvester. When the mean plus one eigenvector model is used, quantitation can be accomplished using the method described by Sharaf and Kowalski [48]. Osten and Kowalski [50] have recently examined the quantitative accuracy of self modeling curve resolution for the analysis of UV absorbance data obtained from a diode array high performance liquid chromatography detector.

Warner, Christian, Davidson, and Callis [51] have used an approach similar to curve resolution which is based on the eigenanalysis of fluorescence emission-excitation matrices. This method makes use of the same assumptions as the Lawton and Sylvester approach, only nonnegative responses and nonnegative quantities of each component are permitted. Warner and co-workers have relaxed these constraints allowing some elements to be slightly below zero in order to account for noise in the experimental data. Since the EEM represents data involving two spectral dimensions, they have considered the uncertainties in the estimated spectra for differing combinations of spectral overlap involving either one or both spectral dimensions between the two pure components.

The problem of generalizing curve resolution from the 2-component situations just described to the N-component case is not trivial. Martens [49] examined the problem of three component mixtures of cereal amino acids. Ohta [52] has shown the solution of the 3-components problem for a mixture of photographic dyes. Very recently, Borgen and Kowalski [53] have described a general solution for the N-component resolution case. In all of these situations, the same nonnegative quantity and nonnegative response constraints have been utilized.

The multivariate methods discussed can be used to improve the precision and accuracy of an analytical procedure. The widespread incorporation of microprocessors in analytical instrumentation can inundate the chemist with raw data. In order to obtain valid chemical information from this wealth of data, the analyst must consider not only the chemical system under evaluation but also the advantages, disadvantages, limits, and assumptions inherent in various potential data analyses approaches. Finally, the reader is again informed that this chapter represents the subject at the time the FACSS symposium was held. The current literature and recent issues of *Fundamental Reviews in Analytical Chemistry* contain further advances in chemometrics.

Acknowledgment

This work was supported in part by the Office of Naval Research and by the National Science Foundation under Grant CHE-8004220.

References

[1] Kowalski, B. R., *Analytical Chemistry,* Vol. 52, 1980, pp. 112R–122R.
[2] Frank, I. E. and Kowalski, B. R., *Analytical Chemistry,* Vol. 54, 1982, pp. 232R–243R.
[3] Kateman, G., Translation in *Analytical Chemistry,* Vol. 3, No. 2, 1983, pp. IX–X.
[4] Draper, N. and Smith, H., *Applied Regression Analysis,* 2nd ed.; Wiley, New York, 1981, Chapter 1.
[5] Nattrella, M. G. "Experimental Statistics," National Bureau of Standards Handbook 91; Government Printing Office, Washington, DC, 1963, Chapter 5.
[6] Agterdenbos, J., *Analytica Chemica Acta,* Vol. 108, 1979, pp. 315–323.
[7] Shewell, C. T., *Analytical Chemistry,* Vol. 32, 1960, p. 1535.
[8] Agterdenbos, J., *Analytica Chemica Acta,* Vol. 132, 1981, pp. 127–137.

[9] Meehan, E. J., *Treatise on Analytical Chemistry*, Part 1, Vol. 7, 2nd ed., Elving, P. J. Ed., Wiley, New York, 1981, Section H, Chapter 2.

[10] Schwartz, L. M., *Analytical Chemistry*, Vol. 51, 1979, pp. 723–727.

[11] Garden, J. S., Mitchell, D. G., and Mills, W. N., *Analytical Chemistry*, Vol. 52, 1980, pp. 2310–2315.

[12] Ratzlaff, K. L., *Analytical Chemistry*, Vol. 51, 1979, pp. 232–235.

[13] Larsen, I. L., Hartmann, N. A., and Wagner, J. J., *Analytical Chemistry*, Vol. 45, 1973, pp. 1511–1513.

[14] Franke, J. P., de Zeeuw, R. A., and Hakkert, R., *Analytical Chemistry*, Vol. 50, 1978, pp. 1374–1380.

[15] Martens, H., Spjøtvoll, E., and Volden, R., *Technometrics*, Vol. 24, 1982, pp. 173–180.

[16] Kaiser, H., *Pure Applied Chemistry*, Vol. 34, 1973, pp. 35–61.

[17] Brown, C. W., Lynch, P. F., Obremski, R. J., and Lavery, D. S., *Analytical Chemistry*, Vol. 54, 1982, pp. 1472–1479.

[18] Maris, M. A., Brown, C. W., and Lavery, D. S., *Analytical Chemistry*, Vol. 55, 1983, pp. 1694–1703.

[19] Kisner, H. J., Brown, C. W., and Kavarnos, G. J., *Analytical Chemistry*, Vol. 55, 1983, pp. 1703–1707.

[20] Massy, W. F., *Journal of the American Statisticians Association*, Vol. 60, 1965, pp. 234–256.

[21] Sjostrom, M., Wold, S., Lindberg, W., Persson, J., and Martens, H., *Anal. Chim. Acta*, Vol. 150, 1983, pp. 61–70.

[22] Joreskog, K. G., *Systems Under Indirect Observation*, H. Wold, Ed. Parts I and II, North Holland, Amsterdam, 1982.

[23] Lindberg, W., Persson, J., and Wold, S., *Analytical Chemistry*, Vol. 55, 1983, pp. 643–648.

[24] Saxberg, B. E. H. and Kowalski, B. R., *Analytical Chemistry*, Vol. 51, 1979, pp. 1031–1038.

[25] Jochum, C., Jochum, P., and Kowalski, B. R., *Analytical Chemistry*, Vol. 53, 1981, pp. 85–92.

[26] Kalivas, J. H., *Analytical Chemistry*, Vol. 55, 1983, pp. 565–567.

[27] Moran, M. G. and Kowalski, B. R., *Analytical Chemistry*, Vol. 56, 1984, pp. 562–569.

[28] Sternberg, J. C., Stillo, H. S., and Schwendeman, R. H., *Analytical Chemistry*, Vol. 32, 1960, pp. 84–90.

[29] Zscheile, F. P., Murray, H. C., Baker, G. A., and Peddicord, R. G., *Analytical Chemistry*, Vol. 34, 1962, pp. 1776–1780.

[30] Haaland, D. M. and Easterling, R. G., *Applied Spectroscopy*, Vol. 36, 1982, pp. 665–673.

[31] Kalivas, J. H. and Kowalski, B. R., *Analytical Chemistry*, Vol. 54, 1982, pp. 560–565.

[32] Kalivas, J. H. and Kowalski, B. R., *Analytical Chemistry*, Vol. 55, 1983, pp. 532–535.

[33] Vandeginste, B., Klaessens, J., and Kateman, G., *Analytica Chimica Acta*, Vol. 150, 1983, pp. 71–86.

[34] Leggett, D. J., *Analytical Chemistry*, Vol. 49, 1977, pp. 276–281.

[35] Gayle, J. B. and Bennett, H. D., *Analytical Chemistry*, Vol. 50, 1978, pp. 2085–2089.

[36] Poulisse, H. N. J., *Analytica Chemica Acta*, Vol. 112, 1979, pp. 361–374.

[37] Seelig, P. F. and Blount, H. N., *Analytical Chemistry*, Vol. 48, 1976, pp. 252–258.

[38] Seelig, P. F. and Blount, H. N., *Analytical Chemistry*, Vol. 51, 1979, pp. 327–337.

[39] Brown, T. F. and Brown, S. D., *Analytical Chemistry*, Vol. 54, 1982, p. 607.

[40] Rutan, S. C. and Brown, S. D., *Analytical Chemistry*, Vol. 55, 1983, pp. 1707–1710.

[41] Warner, I. M., Davidson, E. R., and Christian, G. D., *Analytical Chemistry*, Vol. 49, 1977, pp. 2155–2159.

[42] Ho, C. N., Christian, G. D., and Davidson, E. R., *Analytical Chemistry*, Vol. 50, 1978, pp. 1108–1113.

[43] Ho, C. N., Christian, G. D., and Davidson, E. R., *Analytical Chemistry*, Vol. 52, 1980, pp. 1071–1079.

[44] Ho, C. N., Christian, G. D., and Davidson, E. R., *Analytical Chemistry*, Vol. 53, 1981, pp. 92–98.

[45] McCue, M. and Malinowski, E. R., *Journal Chromatographic Science,* Vol. 21, 1983, pp. 229–234.

[46] Lawton, W. H. and Sylvester, E. A., *Technometrics,* Vol. 13, 1971, pp. 617–633.

[47] Sharaf, M. A. and Kowalski, B. R., *Analytical Chemistry,* Vol. 53, 1981, pp. 518–522.

[48] Sharaf, M. A. and Kowalski, B. R., *Analytical Chemistry,* Vol. 54, 1982, pp. 1291–1296.

[49] Martens, H., *Analytica Chimica Acta,* Vol. 112, 1979, pp. 423–442.

[50] Osten, D. W. and Kowalski, B. R., *Analytical Chemistry,* Vol. 56, 1984, pp. 991–995.

[51] Warner, I. M., Christian, G. D., Davidson, E. R., and Callis, J. B., *Analytical Chemistry,* Vol. 49, 1977, pp. 564–573.

[52] Ohta, N., *Analytical Chemistry,* Vol. 45, 1973, pp. 553–557.

[53] Borgen, O. S. and Kowalski, B. R., *Analytica Chemica Acta,* Vol. 174, 1985, pp. 1–26.

David A. C. Compton,[1] Judith R. Young,[1] Ronald G. Kollar,[1] James R. Mooney,[1] and Jeanette G. Grasselli[1]

Some Applications of Computer-Assisted Quantitative Infrared Spectroscopy

REFERENCE: Compton, D. A. C., Young, J. R., Kollar, R. G., Mooney, J. R., and Grasselli, J. G., "**Some Applications of Computer-Assisted Quantitative Infrared Spectroscopy,**" *Computerized Quantitative Infrared Analysis, ASTM STP 934,* G. L. M^{C}Clure, Ed., American Society for Testing and Materials, Philadelphia, 1987, pp. 36–57.

ABSTRACT: Many of the advantages of a research-grade Fourier transform infrared (FT-IR) instrument arise as a consequence of the powerful minicomputer available as part of the instrument. This computer allows for enhanced treatment of the digital spectroscopic data in order to improve the analytical capabilities. These enhanced treatment methods can be used for improved qualitative analysis (for example, by spectral searching) or quantitative analysis.

Enhanced data treatment techniques routinely used in our laboratory will be discussed, including the advantages and limitations of each method. One particularly useful approach of obtaining quantitative information involves the use of variable ratio spectral subtraction. In this method, the absorbance spectrum of a compound is interactively subtracted from the spectrum of a mixture. The value of the ratio necessary to null out the absorption of the component gives the concentration. "Spectral stripping" involves sequentially subtracting several component spectra from a sample spectrum of a multicomponent mixture. Examples of these two techniques will be shown.

When small concentrations of a component are present in a diluent (for example, oil additives) a 1:1 subtraction of the diluent spectrum from the mixture spectrum yields a difference spectrum of the microcomponent from which quantitative information can be obtained.

Another procedure, useful when examining spectra with overlapping band contours, involves resolution enhancement (deconvolution) of the spectral data prior to quantitation. Using this technique the concentration of carboxylic acid salts have been measured in aromatic oils even though there are overlapping absorptions in the 1600 cm^{-1} region.

KEY WORDS: infrared, quantitative analysis, engine oils, Fourier deconvolution, spectral subtraction, nitrated oils, computerized infrared

[1] Project leader, senior chemist, senior chemist, senior research associate, and director, Corporate Research and Analytical Sciences, respectively, Research and Development Center, Standard Oil, Cleveland, OH 44128.

Part I—A Review of Quantitative Analysis by Infrared

It is certainly appropriate that quantitative analysis by infrared (IR) spectroscopy is receiving so much attention today. It is also a bit ironic. The ability to do quantitative analysis was the driving force in the early 1940s in making infrared a dominant analytical tool in the industrial laboratory. One author's (JGG) first assignment at Standard Oil (not in the 1940s!) was the quantitative analysis of the *iso*-normal paraffin split in petrochemical feedstocks. At the same time, the company was doing ortho-, meta-, and para-xylene multicomponent analysis by matrix inversion and **K**-matrices. So we have come full circle in quantitative analysis by IR spectroscopy with, however, much better levels of accuracy and precision, because of computer assistance.

The petroleum industry has been always a major user of quantitative IR methods. There are, for instance, ASTM standard test methods for measuring various parameters of industrial oils by infrared which originated from industrial procedures. There is an approved ASTM environmental test method for measuring hydrocarbons in water using IR spectroscopy. When this method was established by the petroleum industry over 20 years ago, it was useful down to 0.2 ppm of hydrocarbon. Sophisticated gas chromatography (GC) methods and nuclear magnetic resonance (NMR) spectroscopy surpassed IR as quantitative tools in the 1960s and 1970s for analyses of hydrocarbons and chemicals. Yet in our laboratory in 1974, a team of analytical chemists and spectroscopists was involved in obtaining a Federal Department of Agriculture (FDA) clearance on an acrylonitrile-based resin for food container use [1]. Detection limits of 0.05-ppb acrylonitrile polymer in nonvolatile residues from container extractions were achieved using IR spectroscopy as the analytical method. Quantitative infrared has had a good record, and computer-assisted techniques now promise quantum jumps in its applicability.

The introduction of Fourier transform infrared (FT-IR) spectroscopy, where the computer became an integral part of the instrumental system, afforded a new level of power to the spectroscopist. In 1975, Jack Koenig published an often referenced chart (Fig. 1) in *Applied Spectroscopy* [2] to demonstrate that the combination of data processing with IR spectroscopy offered new potential for quality control and quantitative applications, in addition to new applications in the more conventional areas of identification of unknown samples and following molecular changes. This work, along with early papers by Hirschfeld, led to a resurgence of interest in quantitative analysis by infrared.

New avenues of analysis were made available by computer processing of data. Bob Hannah and others were quick to point up that peak heights as a measure of the intensity of an absorption band could be supplemented by integrated absorption areas, which could be easily obtained. First and

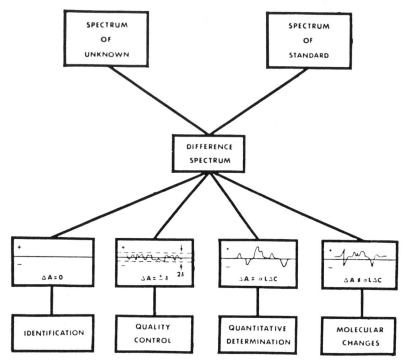

FIG. 1—*Applications of infrared difference spectroscopy (from Ref 1, with permission).*

second derivative information was available and was valuable in certain situations. Quality control methods were set up which could operate in an automated fashion on a 24 h basis. Control limits to the analysis could be set and automatic rejection of outliers would be obtained, permitting later interpretation of spectra of samples which did not meet specifications. Infrared quantitation was relaunched with new vigor—encompassing a new dimension of speed, precision, and accuracy.

But with the computer-aided instruments, papers began to appear quoting the average of 20 "semi-quantitative" determinations as 253.54xx ppm. One must be worried about the analyst who publishes data such as this, just because the number appears on a computer printout. As we will point up in this paper, the power of computer-assisted quantitative IR spectroscopy is attendant with dangers which also must be recognized and dealt with—not the least of these, as will be mentioned time and again, is the analyst.

Let us review for a moment the fundamental law of absorption spectroscopy that governs quantitative analysis

$$A = \sum_i a_i b_i c_i$$

where

A = absorbance = $\log I/I° = \log 1/T$,
a = absorptivity,
b = pathlength, cm, and
c = concentration, mol/m³, kg/m³, g/L

The Bouguer-Beer law is the limiting law for quantitative work in the infrared. For strict adherence to this law, one must be dealing with an infinite dilution of a liquid sample or a gas at very low pressure in an instrument which is working ideally. We also recognize that the IR spectrum of a multicomponent mixture is the additive summation of absorption frequencies for all species present.

For accurate and precise quantitative analysis, one must have photometric linearity and accuracy of the spectrometer. Today's spectrometers can be linear over very large absorbance ranges, 0-3A, if well maintained; and the results they give are very reproducible. But just because we can measure an absorbance up to 3 absorbance units does not imply that one can or should use such intense absorption bands for infrared quantitative analysis. This differs from the situation in ultraviolet (UV) analysis, for example, where one obtains typical absorptivities of 10^3 to 10^5, bands are broad; and one uses dilute solutions and thick cells. In UV analysis, compounds seldom show deviations from the Bouguer-Beer law (or from linearity).

In the infrared, on the other hand, typical absorptivities for bands are much smaller; the bands are sometimes very sharp, and the cells are relatively thin.

This presents a number of problems, not the least of which are much more frequent deviations from Beer's law or nonlinearity of the Beer's law curve. Sources of apparent deviation from the Bouguer-Beer law have been well documented in the literature in excellent texts [3–5]. Table 1 lists some of these.

TABLE 1—*Sources of apparent deviation from Bouguer-Beer law.*

Inhomogeneous sample
    particles/scattering
    anisotropy
    decomposition
Nonreproducible instrument conditions
    reflection losses—liquid cells
    convergence of beam
    peak position
Chemical or physical interaction
    hydrogen bonding
    ion pair formation
    solvation
    chemical reaction

The first problem is undoubtedly the sample itself. It has been said many times, an analysis will only be as good as the sample which has been introduced into the instrument. Small, nonconducting particles suspended in a liquid will show Tyndall scattering. Particles of a sample large enough to make the sample appear inhomogeneous to the beam, or a sample that does not completely fill the beam, will result in very large deviations from the Bouguer-Beer law. Inhomogeneity of the sample or decomposition of the sample during the analysis will also present serious problems.

Some sources of deviation from the Bouguer-Beer law are essentially characteristic of the spectrometer, such as, reflection losses, convergence of the beam, and nonhomogeneity of the incident radiation. Shifts in peak positions for the bands may result from temperature changes in the instrument. Convergence of the sample beam does not ordinarily affect quantitative accuracy unless a beam condenser or microscope attachment is used. As Lee Smith points up in his excellent book on applied infrared spectroscopy [4], one should be aware of problems which can arise from refractive index effects. It is well known that the refractive index of a liquid changes rapidly in the vicinity of a strong absorption band. To minimize refractive index problems, a solution concentration of 2% or less should be used. Also, unless the refractive index of the solvent exactly matches that of the window material of the cell, some reflection loss will take place at the solution window interface, and this may lead to nonreproducible measurements. The refractive index mismatch between solution and cell can also introduce fringe patterns in the spectrum, and these may result in small shifts in the absorption maxima of the bands.

But probably the largest source of deviation from the Bouguer-Beer law arises from chemical or physical interactions in the sample, that is, the failure of the absorbent species to retain its identity. Especially common are phenomena such as hydrogen bonding, ion pair formation, solvation, and chemical reactions of the sample in solution or during analysis. Deviations from the Bouguer-Beer law need not affect quantitative accuracy as long as they are recognized.

Some of the limitations to quantitative accuracy in infrared analysis should be also considered. Table 2 is a summary of some commonly recognized limitations. While photometric linearity is very good in an FT-IR system, we do not completely understand the photometric "accuracy." No one has yet completed a definitive study for FT-IR similar to the classical work which Bryce Crawford and Norman Jones conducted to determine photometric accuracy in dispersive instruments. The International Union of Pure and Applied Chemistry (IUPAC) has commissioned such a study at John Bertie's laboratory at the University of Alberta in Edmonton. A round-robin test on a number of liquids was finished in late 1985, and the results may give an idea of how well we are doing with respect to photometric accuracy of FT-IR instruments.

TABLE 2—*Limitations to quantitative accuracy.*

"Photometric" accuracy
Instrument stability
Software
Noise level
Cells
Sample
Analyst

For FT-IR instruments, factors such as source drift, phase correction errors, how we handle the interferogram, and how we record the data must be understood. Noise levels which affect the data arise not only from the detector, but now also from digitization procedures. Temperature effects in the spectrometer or the sample may change peak intensities or cell pathlengths. It is clear that the precise measurement of cell pathlengths, especially for very thin cells, may be one of the most serious limitations to quantitative accuracy.

Nonhomogeneous samples, difficult to sample materials, or samples subject to chemical or physical interactions may limit the accuracy of an analysis. Infrared methods are subject to nonlinearity of Beer's law, and this is true whether or not the instrument is computerized.

Perhaps the biggest variable in the whole system is the analyst. The person using the spectrometer, even with all the built in quantitative routines, must understand the basis of those routines to determine when something is amiss in the analysis. Eisenhart has said, "Until a measurement operation has attained a state of statistical control, it cannot be regarded in any logical sense as measuring anything at all." We must follow the teachings of John Taylor of the National Bureau of Standards regarding precision, reproducibility, and accuracy of analyses, as well as recognizing the problems of sampling. As Taylor has said time and again, the analytical method can be often more accurate than the sampling method. In today's world, which emphasizes quality assurance and quality control, these all assume great importance.

We have several recommendations for quantitative analysis in the infrared (Table 3). Work at absorbance levels between 0.2 and 0.7 (even if you can measure an absorbance of 2.5 to 3.0!). Integrated band areas are usually

TABLE 3—*Recommendations for good quantitative analysis in the infrared region.*

Keep A between 0.2 and 0.7
Use broad band rather than sharp band
Use bands not sensitive to environment
Use band areas or overdetermination
Check calibration frequently
Watch for temperature effects
Set conditions reproducibility

more precise than are peak height measurements. Use broad bands rather than sharp bands because they are not as susceptible to frequency shifts or lack of reproducibility from apodization or other software variables, as shown by Anderson and Griffiths [9]. Seek bands which are not sensitive to the chemical or physical environment of the sample. Use "overdetermination," a method championed by Chris Brown, which uses a region of the spectrum representative of the sample rather than a single absorption band per component, resulting in a much better general quantitative analysis. Of course, use the computer to help improve your precision and reliability, but check calibrations frequently. Watch for temperature effects, especially when a sample has been in the spectrometer for a long time. Set your conditions reproducibly. The best analysts do the same thing over and over. Finally, "look at your data and *think*"—always, about any computer-assisted method. With these guidelines, and with recognition of error sources, there is no question that quantitative IR analysis is now fast, accurate, and generally applicable to a wide variety of problems. Its "resurrection" is complete.

Part II—Some Examples of Computer Aided Spectroscopy

We would like now to talk about applications of computer-assisted quantitative IR analysis in our laboratories. We will not discuss multicomponent analysis since it is covered in other chapters. The instrumental conditions that were used for the examples described here are shown in Table 4.

Spectral Subtraction

The first example is straight 1:1 subtraction. The problem is the analysis of used motor oils. The procedure is to obtain and compare FT-IR spectra of used and unused oils, noting changes with time. Since the overall composition of the oil changes marginally with time, it is permissible to subtract the spectrum of the unused oil from that of the used oil, using a 1:1 ratio. John Coates and co-workers at Perkin-Elmer have done a lot of work on used oil analysis [6], quantitating it in the infrared (as have we at Standard Oil and most other oil companies) because this has been a problem for a long time. Figure 2 shows the spectrum of the reference oil and the spectrum

TABLE 4—*Instrumental conditions.*

Transmission: Nicolet 7199
Micro IRS: Nicolet 60SX
Resolution: 2 cm^{-1}
   NDP = 8K
   NTP = 16K
MCT B detector (low cutoff 400 cm^{-1})
100 scans
Happ-Genzel apodization
No smoothing

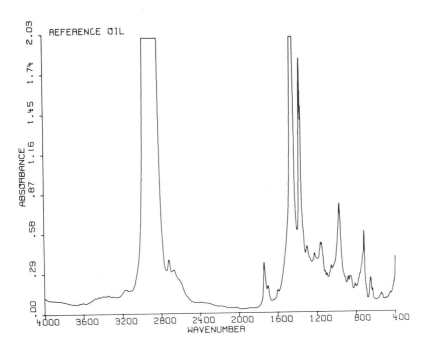

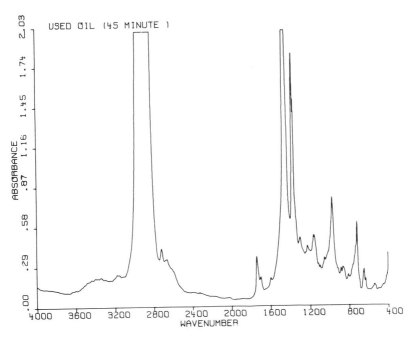

FIG. 2—*Infrared spectra in absorbance of an unused engine oil* (top) *and the same oil after 45 min of use in a test-bed engine* (bottom). *Both spectra were recorded in a 0.1-mm cell. Note that the spectra show no significant differences on inspection.*

of the oil used for only 45 min. Our work varies here from some of the published work which examines oils after several thousand miles of use. We have been trying to set up predictive methods based on the behavior of the oil in the first few minutes of a test engine operation, in order to determine what will happen to the oil in hours of test car driving. There is an advantage if you can look very quickly at the oil and observe components that are going to degrade under use. This will allow the development of better motor oils for the next generation engine.

One can employ spectral subtraction (Fig. 3) and observe changes in the bands due to the base oil, as well as in those due to several of the additives, in the very early stages of oil use. For example, the appearance of the band near 1000 cm^{-1} indicates that a change in the structure of the zinc dithiophosphate wear additive may be occurring during the first few minutes of the engine use. The change in absorption of bands characteristic of certain additives are measured from the subtraction spectra and then plotted against time so that we can observe general trends, as shown in Fig. 4. Other bands, such as that at 1745 cm^{-1} (due to the methacrylate viscosity index improver)

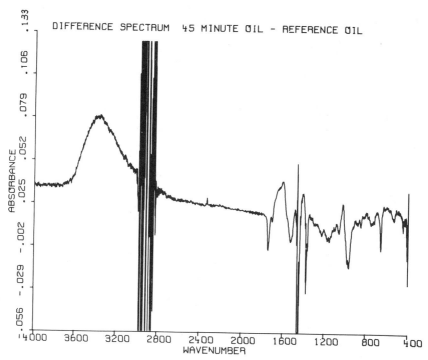

FIG. 3—*Difference spectrum obtained by subtracting the spectrum of the unused engine oil from that of the oil after 45 min of use. A 1:1 subtraction was carried out. Note the very large expansion used on the absorbance scale. The regions at 2900, 1450, and 1380 cm^{-1} should be disregarded due to the strong base oil absorptions at these frequencies.*

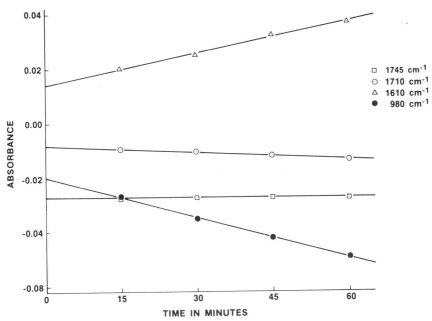

FIG. 4—*Plot of differential absorbances of peaks shown in Fig. 3 versus time of engine run in minutes.*

do not change at all in the early stages of use. One point that is readily apparent from Fig. 4 is that none of the lines on the graph go through the origin. This result is very informative about the initial few minutes of engine use. We attribute the initial drop in additive concentrations in the oil as being due to a coating of the metal surfaces. Cold startup of an engine is known to produce carboxylic acids and water very quickly. A large 3400 cm^{-1} band can be seen in Fig. 3 as well as a band due to acid salt at 1610 cm^{-1}. In addition, any traces of particulate matter in the used oil have the effect of altering the observed baseline slightly, resulting in a zero offset in the difference spectrum.

It should be pointed up that we are working on a very small absorbance scale, 0.1 absorbance units full scale, and we are talking about minutes of engine use. Even so, you can see linear trends in the band intensities that are changing. The band at 1610 cm^{-1} that is increasing with time is particularly interesting. John Coates and others have puzzled about its origin. We think it is due to carboxylic acid salts forming in the early stages, and have additional corroborating evidence for that. In any case, computer aided IR analysis of used oils is reliable, quickly performed, reproducible, and provides useful information on the degradation process.

Another example of 1:1 subtraction is in monitoring the nitration level of oils. It has been found that the level of nitroxidation of an oil is directly

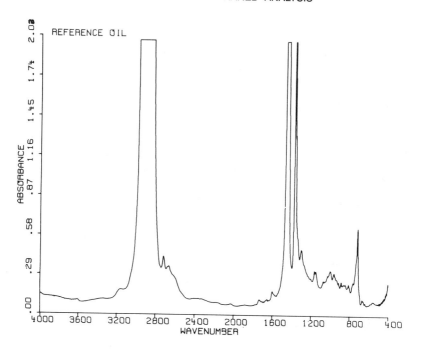

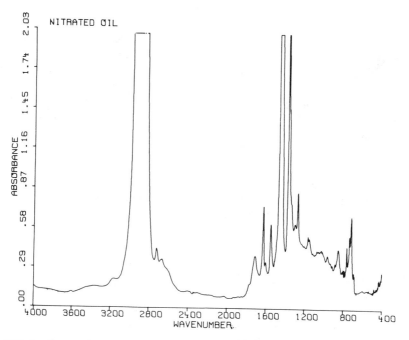

FIG. 5—*Spectra of an untreated sample of a motor oil* (top) *and after nitroxidation treatment* (bottom). *The spectra were recorded in a 0.1-mm cell.*

related to its varnishing and sludging properties [7]. We studied a series of oils to find those with low nitration levels after laboratory treatment. This was done in order to simulate the effects of engine use in the laboratory. The spectra of the reference oil and the nitrated oil are shown in Fig. 5. A one-to-one subtraction is made to obtain the resulting difference spectrum shown in Fig. 6. The bands that have appeared here are due to the nitration of the oil—the carbonyls, the nitrates, and nitro compounds are observed. We find that concentration differences of 0.1% can be detected using these ideal references, so we are looking at very low levels of components. Under more normal conditions, variances in the reference used and other factors substantially degrade confidence levels and the detectability of components, to approximately 1%. Under conditions of extended use we can encounter some interferences.

Variable Subtraction

In another example, it was of interest to obtain an analysis of coker kerosine in tar sands extract. Coker kerosine is used as a solvent to extract bitumen from the tar sands. It is important to know the amount of kerosine

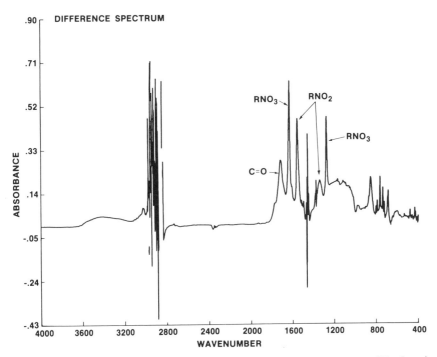

FIG. 6—*Difference spectrum obtained by subtracting the reference oil spectrum* (Fig. 5, top) *from that obtained after nitroxidation. A 1:1 subtraction was performed. The regions at 2900, 1450, and 1380 cm*$^{-1}$ *should be ignored, as for Fig. 3.*

in the extract. The spectra of coker kerosine and of the kerosine/bitumen mixture are shown in Fig. 7. The bands with the arrows are due to the unsaturates in the kerosine. A variable subtraction can be performed using these, since they are not found in the spectrum of the bitumen. The cathode-ray tube (CRT) screen is used for zeroing all those bands to baseline. In doing so, the variable subtraction ratio is obtained, and this equals the quantitative amount of kerosine which then remains in the extracted bitumen. Figure 8 illustrates the subtracted result. From the final subtraction ratio of 0.80 it was determined that there was 80% of kerosine in the fraction. This method was verified through the use of known volumes of kerosine

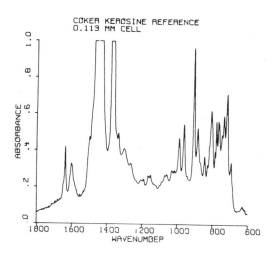

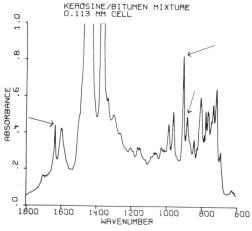

FIG. 7—*Spectra of a reference sample of coker kerosine* (top), *and a coker/kerosine bitumen mixture* (bottom). *The spectra were recorded using a 0.113-mm cell. The arrows point to bands in the spectrum of the mixture that can be used to quantitate the kerosine content.*

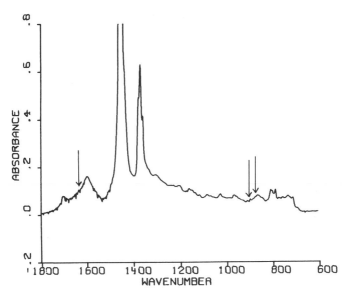

FIG. 8—*Difference spectrum obtained by subtracting the spectrum of coker kerosine from that of the kerosine/tar sands bitumen mixture. The arrowed frequencies are those of the kerosine (see Fig. 7), these have been interactively "zeroed" out using a 0.80 subtraction ratio.*

mixed into the same kind of samples. The results of this comparison are shown in Table 5. One sample is an outlier. It was a very viscous extract that was hard to sample, demonstrating that the sample is indeed one of the concerns with quantitative analysis.

The variable subtraction results were also checked by plotting peak height versus concentration just to be sure this quantitation was giving reliable and realistic values. Figure 9 shows the calibration curve obtained by the classical IR method. The observed straight line was a good verification of the methodology. Therefore, this quantitation can be performed by either variable subtraction or conventional calibration techniques. Subtraction is certainly more convenient; it is interactive on your screen, you can watch it happen, and you get the results faster. The method uses more data points; therefore, it is less subject to interference. However, it only works when the number

TABLE 5—*Test of quantitative accuracy of coker kerosine in tar sands extract by FT-IR.*

Sample	Kerosine as Mixed, volume %	Kerosine Measured, volume %
CAB	79.1	79
CAC	59.5	64
CAE	79.4	80
CAF	88.9	88
CAG	94.8	94

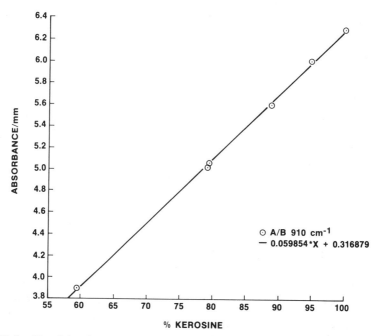

FIG. 9—*Plot of absorbance of the coker kerosine 910 cm^{-1} band (normalized by being divided by the cell pathlength in mm) versus the concentration of kerosine in tar sands extract.*

of components present are known and when the system is well defined. For quantitative analysis, one must always try to think back on the problems of the analysis. Make sure particularly that your client understands where your problems from nonreproducibility or lack of precision arise.

Fourier Deconvolution

Resolution enhancement is another technique that is widely used to improve the analysis of spectroscopic data. This allows you to get improved quantitation of overlapping bands, as long as the resolution enhancement is performed at a conservative level. Fourier deconvolution [8] is particularly useful for resolution enhancement, as the band areas are unchanged by the procedure. This, and the effect of sloping baselines on the area after deconvolution were studied. We used a synthetic Lorentzian lineshape of 20 cm^{-1} halfbandwidth, centered at 1000 cm^{-1}, as our basis data file and measured the area by integration under the curve over the whole region from 1200 to 800 cm^{-1}. This wide region was integrated in order to take in the area of the wings as much as possible. This original file was then deconvolved using a range of halfbandwidths and levels of resolution enhancement (the K-factor). The area of the resulting curve was then also obtained by integration, and the results are shown in Fig. 10 and in Table 6, under the heading "Flat Baseline."

For the flat baseline case, the band area is retained for a Lorentzian-shaped band during deconvolution. Next a series of baselines from gentle to severe slopes was applied to find out whether the area under the band was maintained. In comparing the areas given in Table 6 for the flat and sloping baseline cases, it is clear that there is a discrepancy, since the areas calculated using a sloping baseline appear to alter with deconvolution. This was an unexpected result, and a disturbing one. Since there are three software routines being used here, that is, baseline calculation, integration, and

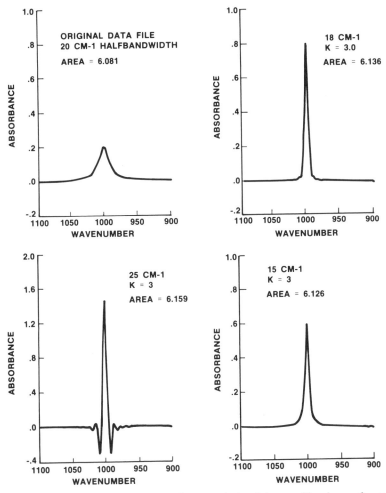

FIG. 10—*The effect of Fourier deconvolution on the band shape and band area of a synthetic Lorentzian line. K represents the resolution enhancement used during deconvolution.*

TABLE 6—*Table of band areas measured after Fourier deconvolution.*

Halfbandwidth	K-Factor	Area[a]
FLAT BASELINE		
Original file		6.081
10	2.5	6.111
10	3.0	6.111
15	1.0	6.127
15	2.0	6.127
15	2.5	6.127
15	3.0	6.126
18	2.5	6.136
18	3.0	6.136
20	2.5	6.143
20	3.0	6.143
25	2.5	6.159
25	3.0	6.159
MEDIUM SLOPE BASELINE		
Original data		5.823
15	3.0	6.113
18	3.0	6.241
20	3.0	6.325
25	3.0	6.537
SEVERE SLOPE BASELINE		
Original data		5.485
18	3.0	6.298
25	3.0	6.615

[a] The slight increase in area with deconvolution arises from the infinite tails to high and low frequencies of the pure Lorentzian lineshape.

deconvolution, we are trying to ascertain where a problem may be arising. The deconvolved spectra appear correct even when a severely sloping baseline is used, so we believe this should give the correct area. This is a problem we are working on in our laboratories and is one that we all need to address, because what we can do by simulation of curves is to define the limits of the analysis and better understand the analytical methods that we are using.

An example of the use of Fourier deconvolution as an aid to quantitation is in the measurement of calcium stearate in oil. As can be seen from the lower spectrum in Fig. 11, the bands at 1575 and 1540 cm^{-1} due to calcium stearate are superimposed on the broad absorption due to the oil matrix. This underlying absorption, along with the 1610 cm^{-1} absorption due to the aromatics in the oil, presents a problem in choosing a baseline for quantitative measurements. Mild deconvolution, gaining a resolution enhancement by only a factor of 2, is shown at the top of Fig. 11. It can be seen that the bands at 1575 and 1540 cm^{-1}, due to the acid salt, are now clearly resolved, thus allowing better measurement for quantitative analysis.

A study of the calcium stearate in oil system was made in order to check the assertion that Fourier deconvolution can be used for quantitation. Stan-

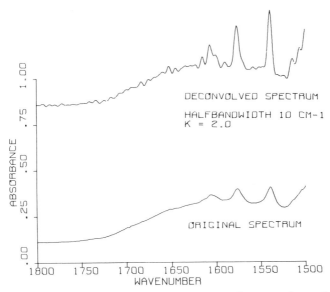

FIG. 11—*Spectrum of calcium stearate in oil. The original spectrum* (bottom) *was deconvolved by using a 10 cm⁻¹ halfbandwidth Lorentzian line, with a resolution enhancement factor of 2.0 to give the result shown at the top.*

dard mixtures of the stearate in oil were examined, and the resulting plot of absorbance versus concentration (Fig. 12) can be seen to be linear over the range of concentrations studied. We checked the work by duplicate sampling and found that the accuracy of measurement was dictated by the accuracy of sampling.

Our conclusions from these studies are that the band areas are not corrupted by deconvolution, at least in the case where no sloping baseline exists; so Fourier deconvolution is a useful aid to quantitation. After deconvolution band areas may be measured, or if preferable the peak heights for a series of similar deconvolved spectra may be measured, as long as the deconvolution factors remain the same for all members of the series. To this end we recommend moderate deconvolution, that is, keeping both the halfbandwidth parameter and the resolution enhancement at a conservative level.

Computer-Assisted Data Analysis

Computer-assisted data analysis is the final example. It can be applied to work which generates lots of data. It can be of tremendous help when looking at many numbers and trying to correctly interpret the results! The computer analysis allows one to enhance quantitation or to follow some particular phenomenon.

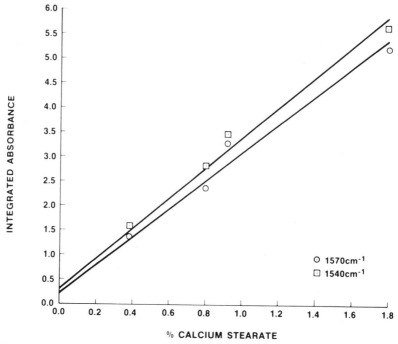

FIG. 12—*Plot of the absorbances of the 1575 and 1540 cm⁻¹ bands of calcium stearate versus the concentration of the stearate in oil. The ordinate scale is in arbitary units of integrated absorbance.*

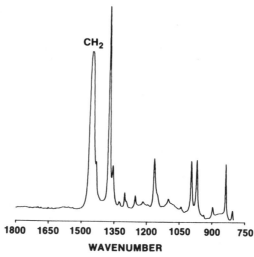

FIG. 13—*Spectrum of a polypropylene film, recorded by using micro IRS and a KRS5 crystal.*

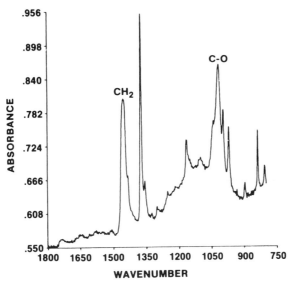

FIG. 14—*Spectrum of an oxidized polypropylene film, recorded by using micro IRS.*

We have been looking at the behavior of a large number of polypropylene films being examined for potential use as membrane separators in small capacitors. It was necessary to ascertain if the films interact with the separator membrane fluids, which can be strong acids. As a test, some experimental films were submitted to a series of oxygen exposure experiments. It was difficult to extract useful information from the large amount of data obtained—we were just overwhelmed with numbers. The experiment was done using micro (IRS) internal reflection spectroscopy, since we wanted to look just at the surface of these separators. The spectra of unoxidized and oxidized films are shown in Figs. 13 and 14. Good quality spectra were obtained very rapidly by the micro IRS technique. From the spectra that were recorded, peak heights from various bands in the spectra were tabulated. The computer was used to select the bands that showed significant change, in terms of the oxygen uptake of the film. It was found that the ratio of the carbon-oxygen stretching band height at 1020 cm^{-1} to that of the methylene (CH_2) band at 1450 cm^{-1} could be correlated with oxidation properties. By examination of these calculated ratios versus sample number (Fig. 15), it was possible to quickly pick out the film properties; and now this becomes a nice, fast method in the exploratory stages of a research project. Samples that are being affected can be quickly identified. So computer analysis of the large sets of data allowed easier interpretation and improved deductions to be made.

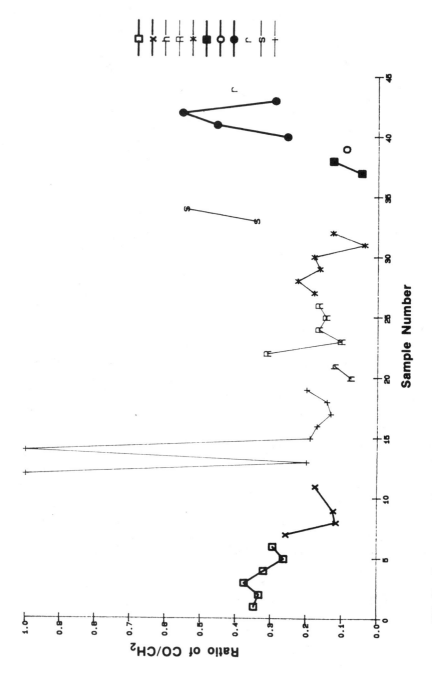

FIG. 15—*Computer-assisted tabulation of the 1450/1010 absorbance ratios for several sets of oxidized polypropylene films.*

Acknowledgment

The authors wish to thank J. L. O'Kane for the micro IRS spectra and work on the polypropylene films.

References

[1] Gaylor, V. F., *Analytical Chemistry,* Vol. 46, No. 11, 1974, p. 897A.
[2] Koenig, J. L., *Applied Spectroscopy,* Vol. 29, 1975, p. 293.
[3] Bauman, R. P., *Absorption Spectroscopy,* Wiley, New York, 1962.
[4] Smith, A. L., *Applied Infrared Spectroscopy,* Wiley, New York, 1979.
[5] Potts, W. J., *Chemical Infrared Spectroscopy,* Wiley, New York, 1962.
[6] Coates, J. P. and Setti, L. C., Society for Automotive Engineers Technical Paper Series, Paper No. 831681, 1983.
[7] Kawaguchi, M., Isoda, T., Tamai, K., and Takezawa, Y., *Proceedings,* International Lubrication Conference, Japan, 1975, p. 758.
[8] Kauppinen, J. K., Moffatt, D. J., Mantsch, H. H., and Cameron, D. G., *Applied Spectroscopy,* Vol. 35, 1981, p. 271.
[9] Anderson, R. J. and Griffiths, P. R., *Analytical Chemistry,* Vol. 50, No. 13, 1978, p. 1804.

Harry A. Willis,[1] *John M. Chalmers,*[2] *Moray W. Mackenzie,*[2] *and David J. Barnes*[3]

Novel Quantitative Polymer Analysis Through Computerized Infrared Spectroscopy

REFERENCE: Willis, H. A., Chalmers, J. M., Mackenzie, M. W., and Barnes, D. J., "**Novel Quantitative Polymer Analysis Through Computerized Infrared Spectroscopy,**" *Computerized Quantitative Infrared Analysis, ASTM STP 934,* G. L. MᶜClure, Ed., American Society for Testing and Materials, Philadelphia, 1987, pp. 58–77.

ABSTRACT: Infrared quantitative analysis of synthetic polymers can be improved in convenience, speed, and precision by the use of computer methods. Examples are given of applications using dispersive and Fourier transform spectrometers and a near-infrared analyser. Measurements include transmittance, specular and diffuse reflectance, and photo-acoustic spectra.

KEY WORDS: computers, spectrometers, Fourier transform infrared (FT-IR), dispersive infrared, near infrared, transmittance, specular reflectance, diffuse reflectance, photoacoustic, derivative spectroscopy, difference spectroscopy, thermal radiative properties, quantitative analysis

Most modern infrared spectrophotometers incorporate a microcomputer or dedicated data system both for instrument control and for data acquisition and manipulation. These can substantially reduce the time for the characterization of samples and for the calculation of results in quantitative analyses.

Unfortunately little has been achieved in reducing the time taken to prepare samples. This is of particular significance for synthetic polymers, where a major proportion of the time spent on analysis is in sample preparation. Use of simplified sampling procedures, made possible because of

---

[1] Formerly, research associate, Imperial Chemical Industries plc; presently, 4 Sherrardspark Road, Welwyn Garden City, Herts, U.K.

[2] Research physicists, Research and Technology Department, Petrochemicals and Plastics Division, Imperial Chemical Industries plc, Wilton, Middlesbrough, Cleveland, U.K.

[3] Research physicist, Technical Department, Mond Division, Imperial Chemical Industries plc, The Heath, Runcorn, Cheshire, U.K.

improvements in performance from incorporating a computer, is considered in the present work, as well as other aspects of polymer analysis which can be more conveniently handled by taking advantage of a data processing system.

Direct Measurement of Samples Presented As Powders Or Granules

Most polymers are produced in either powder or granular form. In these forms they are not readily amenable to measurement by conventional transmission spectroscopy and have to be cast from solution or compression moulded into thin films before infrared examination is possible. In some cases this is not possible or is time consuming. However, sampling times would be considerably reduced if these materials could be examined directly.

Present computerized spectrophotometers, either dispersive or Fourier transform, have the ability to produce spectra whose signal-to-noise ratio is sufficiently high to enable infrared measurements to be made by diffuse reflectance [1]. We have investigated methods by which spectra, measured directly on polymer powders as manufactured, may be used for satisfactory quantitative analysis.

Unless a sample can be presented as a very thin layer of a fine powder [2] the spectrum measured in the fingerprint region (<1500 cm^{-1}) may have the appearance of a transmission spectrum measured on a sample which is too thick to be of use in quantitative analysis. Although this problem in the mid-infrared region can be overcome by diluting the powder in a nonabsorbing matrix such as potassium chloride (KCl), often a more practical solution is to make measurements in the near-infrared region (10 000 to 3000 cm^{-1}) where the absorption bands characteristic of particular molecular groupings are intrinsically much weaker [3].

Figure 1 shows the diffuse reflectance spectra of poly(vinyl chloride) and two vinyl chloride/vinyl acetate copolymers in the range 5000 to 2500 cm^{-1}. These spectra have been measured directly on the polymer as produced in powder form at "infinite depth" [1]. The composition of the copolymer powders had been determined independently and allowed the samples to be used as homogeneous calibration standards. The ordinate axis in Fig. 1 is simply proportional to the radiation reflected, R. Alternatively the spectral data may be expressed in terms of the relationship derived by Kubelka and Munk [4]. However, in this case no significant difference was found between use of the Kubelka-Munk function and use of R in a Beer's law expression of the form

$$\log_{10} \frac{1}{R} = Ecl$$

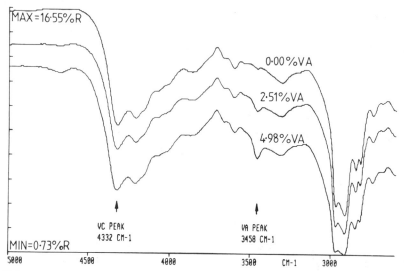

FIG. 1—*Diffuse reflectance infrared spectra of poly(vinyl chloride) powder and two vinyl chloride/vinyl acetate copolymer powders.*

where

E = a constant
c = concentration of component sought
l = sample thickness

The two bands chosen for the determination of the proportions of vinyl chloride (VC) to vinyl acetate (VA) were 4332 cm^{-1} (VC) and 3458 cm^{-1} (VA), with background reference points at 4600 and 3568 cm^{-1}, respectively. The calculation, which can be readily computerized, is effectively that of a "double overlap" analysis [5], applicable when the thickness of the samples cannot be measured and is not necessarily the same for all samples, as is the case in diffuse reflectance measurements where even at "infinite depth" signal strength is influenced by particle size and packing.

TABLE 1—*Determination of copolymerized vinyl acetate content in vinyl chloride/vinyl acetate copolymer powders by diffuse reflectance.*

Expected %VA	Determined %VA
0.0	0.0
2.5	2.5
5.0	5.0
7.5	7.6
15.0	15.0

The results obtained on the samples of known VA content are given in Table 1. The precision of the diffuse reflectance measurement is estimated to be ±0.1% VA. The data contained in Table 1 demonstrate the excellent quality of the results which can be obtained by direct measurement of powder samples by diffuse reflectance. These measurements were taken with a ratio recording dispersive spectrophotometer (Perkin Elmer 983) using a Harrick diffuse reflectance attachment.

Another copolymer system (vinylidene chloride/acrylonitrile) was examined with a microprocessor-controlled scanning near infrared analyser (Technicon Infra Alyser 500) [6] which incorporates an integrating sphere as the means by which diffusely scattered radiation is collected. The spectral region examined (7000 to 3700 cm^{-1}) overlaps that of the Perkin Elmer 983, but the near-infrared analyser is calibrated in wavelength (nm) rather than wavenumber (cm^{-1}).

With the Technicon 500 it is possible to select the analytical wavelengths manually, or to allow the computer to select the wavelengths based on the best mathematical fit to a linear regression analysis of all the available

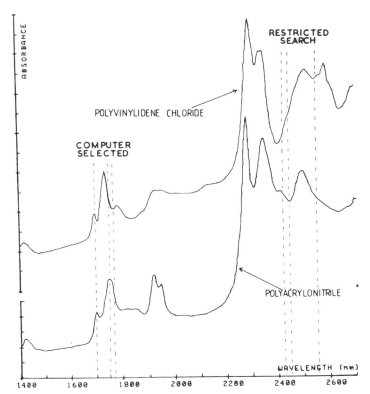

FIG. 2—*Diffuse reflectance infrared spectra of polyacrylonitrile and poly(vinylidene chloride) homopolymer powders.*

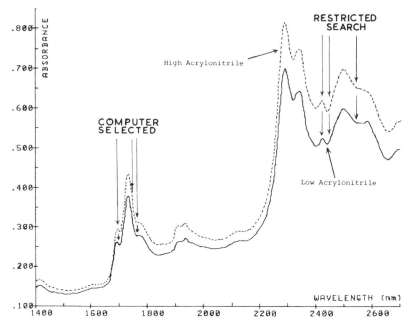

FIG. 3—*Diffuse reflectance infrared spectra of two vinylidene chloride/acrylonitrile co-polymer powders.*

chemical and spectroscopic data. In either case it is necessary to have a relatively large number of calibration samples in order to obtain a statistically significant result.

With reference to the near-infrared diffuse reflectance spectra of the two homopolymers in powder form (Fig. 2), analytical wavelengths were selected by inspection (restricted search), and automatically by computer by obtaining the best fit to a set of eleven standard copolymers. Figure 3 shows the near-infrared diffuse reflectance spectra of two copolymer powders. In these spectra the ordinate axis is $\log_{10} 1/R$. Figures 4 and 5 compare the known and calculated copolymer compositions using computer and operator selected wavelengths respectively. The abscissa (actual) axes are related to independent measurements of copolymer composition and represent the property value to which the spectroscopic data are correlated. The analytical wavelengths used in the correlations are also shown in Figs. 4 and 5. The ordinate axes predict the property value obtained from all available chemical and spectroscopic data. The precision in terms of the standard error of the estimate is higher in the case of the computer selected wavelengths (see Figs. 4 and 5), implying that, except in cases where key bands can be chosen on good spectroscopic grounds (for example, the selection of $2\bar{\nu}$ ($C = 0$) at 3458 cm^{-1} for copolymerized vinyl acetate), selection by computer may well be preferred. However, the onus remains on the operator to ensure that the chemical data are sound and that the analytical wavelengths selected by the computer are valid and not due to some 'impurity' [for example, H-bonded water (H_2O)] which may vary in concentration at some time in the future.

The success of diffuse reflectance measurements in the near-infrared region led us to look at the possibility of applying this technique to the quantitative analysis of tetrafluoroethylene/hexafluoropropylene (TFE/HFP) copolymer powders using the relatively weak absorption bands at 980 cm^{-1} (HFP) and 935 cm^{-1} (TFE) [2]. Spectra of several TFE/HFP copolymers are shown in Fig. 6. In this case the calibration graph is linear using the

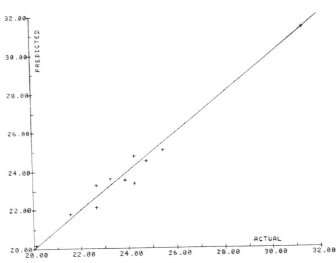

COMPUTER SELECTED λ's

Wavelength	Regression Coefficient	t value of Coefficient
intercept	54.498	
1755	1495.100	15.177464
1775	-1617.140	-13.835985
1700	76.042	2.526415

Multiple Correlation Coefficient	=	.986653
Standard Error of Estimate	=	.523457

FIG. 4—*Linear regression analysis of spectroscopic data on a series of vinylidene chloride/ acrylonitrile copolymers using computer selected wavelength. The axes are related to copolymer composition* (see text).

RESTRICTED SEARCH λ's

Wavelength	Regression Coefficient	t value of Coefficient
intercept	56.095	
2425	3274.948	5.958556
2455	-3925.325	-8.555193
2560	479.023	1.154795

```
Multiple Correlation Coefficient   =        .957576
Standard Error of Estimate         =        .926389
```

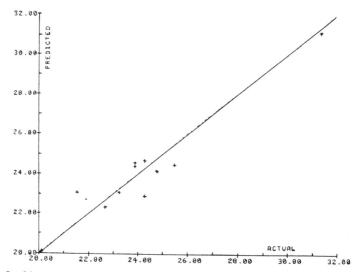

FIG. 5—*Linear regression analysis of spectroscopic data on a series of vinylidene chloride/ acrylonitrile copolymers using operator selected wavelengths. The axes are related to copolymer composition (see text).*

Kubelka-Munk function. The calibration graph is shown in Fig. 7 and indicates that diffuse reflectance is a satisfactory method of measuring the copolymerized HFP content of these copolymer powders. It should be noted, however, that weak absorption bands relatively close in wavenumber were chosen for the determination and that the powders were of a uniform particle size. For measuring the Kubelka-Munk ratio, a background was drawn between the minima near 1010 and 880 cm^{-1} on the spectra shown in Fig. 6, and the peak heights at 980 and 935 cm^{-1} calculated.

Photo-acoustic spectroscopy (PAS) is also recognized as a technique by which infrared spectra can be measured directly on powders [7]. When applied to samples of "infinite depth" photo-acoustic spectroscopy appears to measure a considerably smaller "optical thickness" than diffuse reflec-

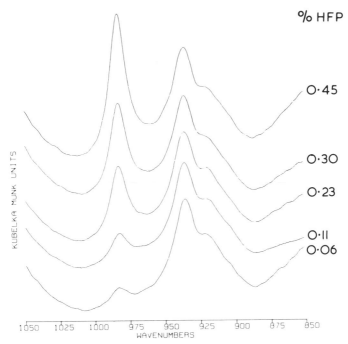

FIG. 6—*Diffuse reflectance infrared spectra of tetrafluoroethylene/hexafluoropropylene co-polymer powders. Spectra recorded on a Nicolet 170SX Fourier transform spectrometer.*

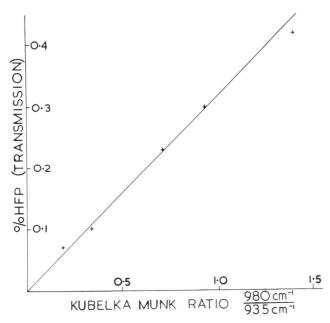

FIG. 7—*Comparison of compositional results on tetrafluoroethylene/hexafluoropropylene copolymers determined by transmission and diffuse reflectance techniques.*

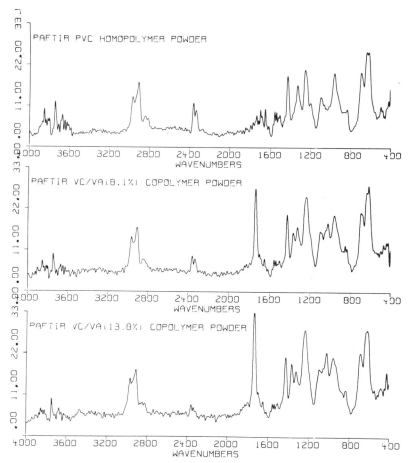

FIG. 8—*Photoacoustic infrared spectra of poly(vinyl chloride) powder and two vinyl chloride/ vinyl acetate copolymer powders. Spectra recorded on Nicolet 170SX Fourier transform spectrometer. Reproduced from Ref 7 by permission of the Royal Society of Chemistry.*

tance spectroscopy [8]; hence, it should be applicable to analyses based on intrinsically more intense absorption bands. Thus vinyl chloride/vinyl acetate (VC/VA) copolymers in powder form give satisfactory spectra in the fingerprint region, see Fig. 8. In these spectra the ordinate axes are given by the expression

$$\frac{\text{signal from sample}}{\text{signal from powdered carbon black}} \times 100$$

Although it is well known that the intensity (signal strength) of the PAS spectrum of a powder depends on the particle size of the powder [8], the ratio of the peak height of absorption bands close in wavenumber and of similar optical absorption coefficient should be virtually independent of particle size. A plot of the ratio of peak heights at 1430 and 1378 cm^{-1} from the spectra of a series of VC/VA copolymers is given in Fig. 9. This is shown as a smooth curve, although for a similar case because of band overlap, Rockley et al [9] considered that such a relationship might be a straight line with a positive intercept on the ordinate axis. In either event the treatment would appear to be reasonable for semi-quantitative analysis, but it would seem unlikely that a precision would be achieved as good as that found for diffuse reflectance measurements.

Data Manipulation In Quantitative Analysis

In instances where the most useful absorption bands for quantitative analysis are very closely spaced in wavenumber (or wavelength), the appearance of the spectrum can be improved by increasing the apparent resolution of the bands by data manipulation procedures such as resolution enhancement [10] or measuring the spectrum in first, second, or fourth derivative mode. However, we have seldom found it advantageous to use these procedures in quantitative analyses, since they often become signal-to-noise limited, and only appear to work well in particular circumstances. In cases where these data manipulation routines have proved to be valuable

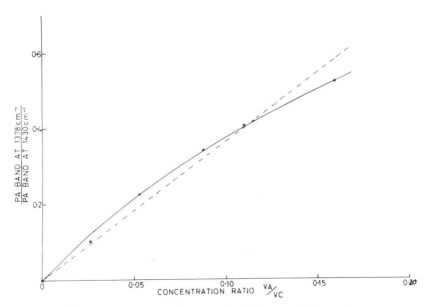

FIG. 9—*Photoacoustic (PA) infrared spectra of vinyl chloride/vinyl acetate copolymer powders: Graph of PA band at 1378 cm^{-1}/PA band at 1430 cm^{-1} against concentration ratio.*

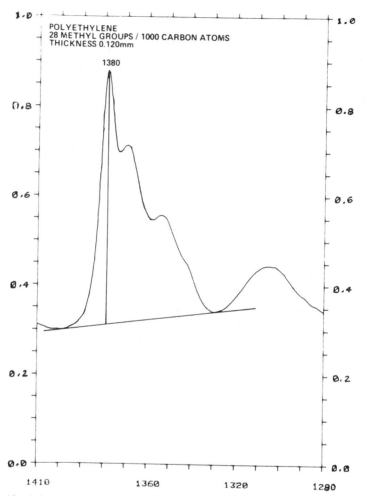

FIG. 10—*Infrared spectra of polyethylene containing 28 methyl groups per 1000 Carbon atoms. Spectrum recorded on Perkin Elmer 683 dispersive infrared spectrometer. Reproduced from Ref 14.*

it is useful if the computer program includes a comparison of the errors found for the different procedures.

An example of the application of derivative methods is in the determination of the methyl group concentration in low-density polyethylene. This involves the measurement of the symmetric deformation vibration of the methyl group at 1380 cm^{-1} which appears on the side of a pair of bands due to the methylene group at 1366 and 1355 cm^{-1} (Fig. 10) [11]. These latter bands are due to methylene groups in polymer chains in the gauche conformation, and, in a particular sample of polyethylene, their intensity will vary according to the thermal history of the sample.

The historic way of dealing with this problem has been to subtract the absorption due to methylene groups by placing in the reference beam of a double beam spectrophotometer a sample of polymethylene whose thickness is chosen so that it cancels exactly the methylene absorption bands (Fig. 11). This was conveniently done by making the polymethylene sample in the form of a wedge [12,13]. This difference spectrum can be now achieved more conveniently by appropriate scaling of the polymethylene spectrum within the computer so that the methylene absorptions cancel.

However, it is seen from Fig. 10 that the symmetric deformation vibration of the methyl group occurs on the steep edge of the methylene band at 1366 cm^{-1}. If the increase in absorbance across this edge is approximately constant, then in the first derivative mode it will be replaced by a horizontal straight line, and the height of the first maximum in the first derivative curve

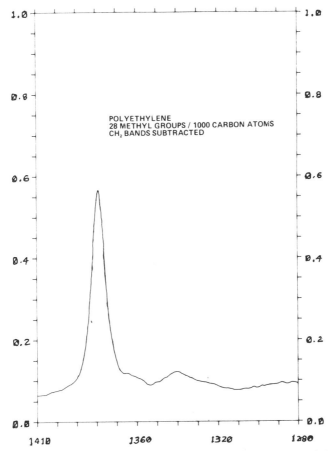

FIG. 11—*Infrared spectrum of polyethylene, CH$_2$ absorption bands subtracted. Reproduced from Ref 14.*

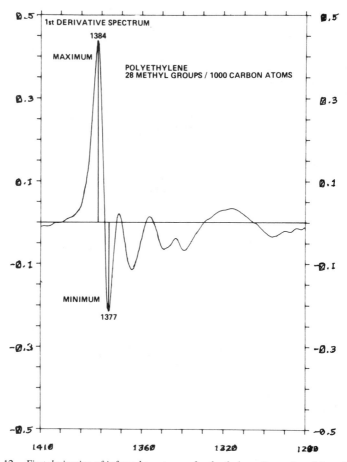

FIG. 12—*First derivative of infrared spectrum of polyethylene. Reproduced from Ref 14.*

TABLE 2—*Determination of methyl groups in polyethylene.[a]*

Method	Error Index, %	
	Original Spectrum	CH_2 Band Subtracted
Peak height 1379 cm^{-1}	2.6	3.1
Peak area 1372 to 1395 cm^{-1}	3.0	3.5
1st derivative maximum	1.6	1.3
1st derivative minimum	5.0	5.3
2nd derivative	2.1	3.5

[a] Reproduced from Ref *14* by kind permission of Perkin Elmer Ltd, Beaconsfield, U.K.

can be measured and related to the methyl content (Fig. 12). Similarly the first minimum in the derivative curve can be used. Measurements can be also made on the second derivative curve [14].

The results of measuring the spectrum by a number of different methods are compared in Table 2. It will be seen that measuring in the first derivative mode is preferred in this instance giving results significantly better than could be achieved by the original difference method.

In some other cases involving the measurement of shoulders on strong bands no advantage is found on using a derivative spectrum, and, in general, it would seem that the various data manipulation techniques should be tried and the most effective one selected by comparing the error indices obtained.

Difference Spectroscopy In Quantitative Analysis

Difference spectra are much more easily measured when computer data handling is available since individual spectra can be readily scaled to eliminate the absorption bands of one component from the spectrum of a mixture. Furthermore, when the unwanted component has an intense spectrum, the signal-to-noise ratio of the difference spectrum can be improved by improving that of the original data by spectrum accumulation [15].

An example of this in a polymeric system is the investigation of the action of dibutyltin bis(isooctyl thioglycollate) in the thermal stabilization of poly(vinyl chloride) (PVC). To be effective organotin stabilizers are believed to replace potentially active sites on the polymer chain [16–18] and react with hydrogen chloride (HCl) evolved during processing due to the thermal decomposition of PVC. However, recent evidence indicates that this particular stabilizer acts primarily as an HCl acceptor [19]. Possible reaction mechanisms are considered to be

$$Bu_2SnY_2 + 2HCl \longrightarrow Bu_2SnCl_2 + 2HY \qquad (1)$$

$$Bu_2SnY_2 + Bu_2SnCl_2 \longrightarrow 2Bu_2SnYCl \qquad (2)$$

$$Bu_2SnY_2 + HCl \longrightarrow Bu_2SnYCl + HY \qquad (3)$$

$$Bu_2SnYCl + HCl \longrightarrow Bu_2SnCl_2 + HY \qquad (4)$$

In these equations $Y = SCH_2CO_2i\text{-Oct}$.

If in the initial stages of processing reactions (1) and (2) were favored over reaction (3), there would be a relatively high concentration of dibutyltin dichloride (Bu_2SnCl_2) which would then decrease, with an increase in the concentration of the monochloride species (Bu_2SnYCl).

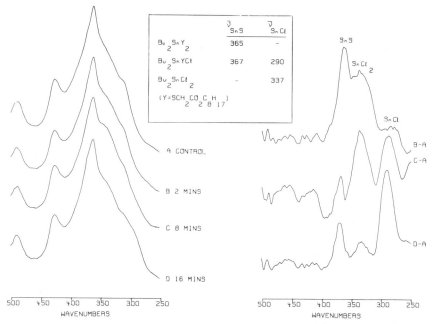

FIG. 13—*Far infrared spectra of dibutyltin bis(isooctyl thioglycollate) stabilized poly(vinyl chloride): Effect of thermal processing. Spectra recorded on Nicolet 170SX Fourier transform spectrometer.*

   In order to follow this reaction by infrared spectroscopy it is necessary to observe the tin-chlorine (SnCl) stretching modes of vibration which absorb in the vicinity of 300 cm^{-1} [20]. Unfortunately PVC itself (Fig. 13, Spectrum A) has intense absorptions in this region due to CCCl bending modes. Spectra of PVC containing the stabilizer after various processing times at 180°C are shown in Fig. 13 as plots B, C, and D. These give little information about the generation of the mono- and dichloride salts of the thioglycollate stabilizer during processing. However, the difference spectra, also shown in Fig. 13, obtained by subtracting the spectrum of pure PVC (Spectrum 13A) from each of the other spectra, exhibit maxima assigned to SnS, SnCl$_2$ plus SnCl stretching vibrations [20]. The normalized absorbances of the mono- and dichloride species are shown in Fig. 14 as a function of processing time. For the dichloride, this shows there is a higher concentration in the earlier stages of processing which decreases to a minimum at about 16 min before increasing once more. This is accompanied by a corresponding increase in the concentration of the monochloride species and suggests that the mechanism initially follows Eqs 1 and 2 rather than 3. The data are consistent with Bu$_2$SnCl$_2$ being formed during the early stages of processing, presumably by reaction of Bu$_2$SnY$_2$ with the HCl generated as gelation takes place. The concentration of the stabilizer can be followed by monitoring the intensity of the intermolecularly bonded carbonyl group absorption at 1705 cm^{-1}. This species virtually disappears after 16 min processing, and it is interesting to note that at this stage the monochloride content begins to fall, while the dichloride content rises, following Eq 4.

The reaction can be also followed quantitatively using coulometry. From Fig. 15 it can be seen that reasonable agreement is obtained between the chloride ion concentration measured coulometrically and the Bu$_2$SnYCl concentration measured spectroscopically [19].

From this it can be concluded that weak bands underlying more intense absorptions can be measured with good precision using difference spectroscopy by computer subtraction of high signal-to-noise spectra.

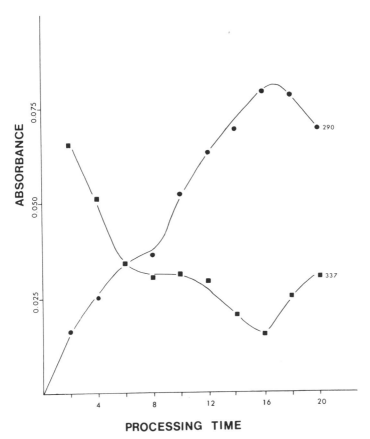

FIG. 14—Bu_2SnYCl (290 cm^{-1}) and Bu_2SnCl_2 (337 cm^{-1}) concentration in dibutyltin bis(isooctyl thioglycollate) stabilized poly(vinyl chloride) as a function of processing time.

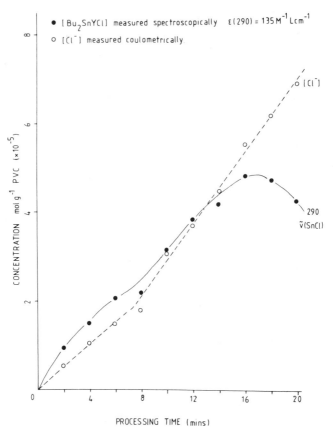

FIG. 15—*Comparison of spectroscopic measurement of Bu₂SnYCl concentration and chloride ion concentration measured coulometrically as a function of processing time in dibutyltin bis(isooctyl thioglycollate) stabilized poly(vinyl chloride).*

Thermal Radiative Properties of Polymer Films

Polymer films are now used widely in horticultural applications such as greenhouse glazing and thermal screening. The thermal radiative properties of these films are clearly important in assessing the effectiveness of the materials, particularly when compared to glass. With the transmission and reflection spectra of glass and plastic films available, it is possible to calculate the thermal radiative properties from Kirchoff's law. To facilitate the calculation we have written a computer program by means of which the proportion of heat transmitted and reflected may be calculated for an emitter at a particular temperature [21].

Transmittance spectra for some materials used are given in Fig. 16. Such spectra, together with the corresponding reflectance spectra, enable the

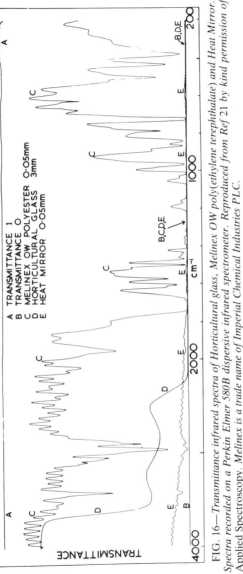

FIG. 16—*Transmittance infrared spectra of Horticultural glass, Melinex OW poly(ethylene terephthalate) and Heat Mirror. Spectra recorded on a Perkin Elmer 580B dispersive infrared spectrometer. Reproduced from Ref 21 by kind permission of Applied Spectroscopy. Melinex is a trade name of Imperial Chemical Industries PLC.*

TABLE 3—*Optical properties of material in respect of thermal radiation (15°C).*[a]

	Transmittance	Reflectance	Absorptance
Glass, 3 mm	0.001	0.112	0.887
Ethylene/propylene copolymer, 0.14 mm	0.736	0.064	0.200
Ethylene/vinyl acetate copolymer, 0.19 mm	0.358	0.043	0.599
Polyester, 0.05 mm	0.330	0.088	0.528
Heat Mirror,[b] 0.05 mm			
Treated surface towards source	0.003	0.893	0.104
Untreated surface towards source	0.003	0.239	0.758

[a] Range, 4000 to 200 cm^{-1}.
[b] Heat Mirror is the trademark of Southwall Technologies, 1029 Corporation Way, Palo Alto, California, U.S.A.

figures given in Table 3 to be calculated for a radiation source at 15°C, which is presumed to be the temperature within the greenhouse. Although the radiative properties of 50-μm-thickness polyester films are slightly poorer than those of 3-mm glass [21] the application of a reflective coating [22] (Heat Mirror) to the polyester film produces a material which reflects up to about 90% of thermal radiation.

Conclusion

Examples have been given of a number of ways in which computerized infrared spectroscopy can be applied to the analysis of synthetic polymers. The examples include simplified sample preparation procedures, application of data manipulation, difference spectroscopy, and the measurement of the thermal radiative properties of films. In each case the availability of the data handling system enabled quantitative analyzes to be carried out relatively simply. In some cases the spectroscopist must judge which is the most appropriate method of analysis, in others which mathematical procedure yields the most reliable information. Since there is always a tendency for numbers generated by a computer to be believed the responsibility lies with the experienced spectroscopist to ensure the correct approach is adopted.

Acknowledgments

We should like to acknowledge I. Robertson of Perkin Elmer Ltd, Beaconsfield, U.K. for assistance with some of the diffuse reflectance measurements and Dr. R. Spragg also of Perkin Elmer Ltd for the computer program used to produce the data given in Table 1.

References

[1] Fuller, M. P. and Griffiths, R. P., *Analytical Chemistry*, Vol. 50, 1978, p. 1906.
[2] (*a*) Chalmers, J. M. and Mackenzie, M. W., Paper 2.18, 1983 International Conference on Fourier Transform Spectroscopy, Durham, England, 5–9 Sept. 1983. (*b*) Chalmers,

J. M. and Mackenzie, M. W., *Applied Spectroscopy,* Vol. 39, 1985, p. 634. (*c*) Spragg, R. A., *Applied Spectroscopy,* Vol. 38, 1984, p. 604.

[*3*] Kaye, W., *Spectrochimica Acta,* Vol. 4, 1954, p. 257.

[*4*] Kubelka, P., *Journal of the Optical Society of America,* Vol. 38, No. 5, 1948, p. 448.

[*5*] Beaven, G. H., Johnson, E. A., Willis, H. A., and Miller, R. G. J., *Molecular Spectroscopy,* Heywood & Co, London, 1961, p. 297.

[*6*] Fearn, F. R. B., *Laboratory Practice,* July 1982, p. 658.

[*7*] Chalmers, J. M., Stay, B. J., Kirkbright, G. F., Spillane, D. E. M., and Beadle, B. C., *The Analyst,* Vol. 106, 1981, p. 1179.

[*8*] Rockley, N. L., Woodward, M. K., and Rockley, M. G., *Applied Spectroscopy,* Vol. 38, 1984, p. 329.

[*9*] Rockley, M. G., Davis, D. M., and Richardson, H. H., *Applied Spectroscopy,* Vol. 35, 1981, p. 185.

[*10*] (*a*) Kauppinen, J. K., Moffatt, D. J., Mantsch, H. H., and Cameron, D. G., *Applied Spectroscopy,* Vol. 35, 1981, p. 271. (*b*) Compton, D. A. C., Mooney, J. R., and Maddams, W. F., Paper 4.14, 1983 International Conference on Fourier Transform Spectroscopy, Durham, England, 5–9 Sept. 1983.

[*11*] Willbourn, A. H., *Journal of Polymer Science,* Vol. 34, 1959, p. 569.

[*12*] Haslam, J., Willis, H. A., and Squirrell, D. C. M., *Identification and Analysis of Plastics,* Wiley, Chichester, U.K. 1972, p. 375.

[*13*] Absorbance of Polyethylene due to Methyl Groups at 1378 cm^{-1}, Standard Method D 2238-64, *1975 Annual Book of ASTM Standards,* pp. 652–699.

[*14*] Chalmers, J. M., Willis, H. A., Cowell, G. M., and Spragg, R. A., Perkin Elmer Infrared Bulletin No. 99, Perkin Elmer, Beaconsfield, U.K., 1982.

[*15*] *Transform Techniques in Chemistry,* P. R. Griffiths, Ed., Heyden & Son Ltd, London, U.K., 1978.

[*16*] Ayrey, G., Head, B. C., and Poller, R. C., *Macromolecular Reviews,* Vol. 8, 1974, p. 1.

[*17*] Ayrey, G. and Poller, R. C., in *Developments in Polymer Stabilisation—2,* G. Scott, Ed., Elsevier, New York, 1980.

[*18*] Poller, R. C., *Journal of Macromolecular Science Chemistry,* Vol. A12, 1978, p. 373.

[*19*] Owen, R. C., Mackenzie, M. W., and Michel, A., to be published.

[*20*] Adams, D. M., *Metal Ligands and Related Vibrations,* Arnold, London, 1967.

[*21*] Stay, B. J., Chalmers, J. M., Mackenzie, M. W., and Mosley, D. R., *Applied Spectroscopy,* Vol. 39, 1985, p. 412.

[*22*] Fan, J. C. C. and Bachner, R. J., *Applied Optics,* Vol. 15, 1976, p. 1012.

David M. Haaland[1]

Methods to Include Beer's Law Nonlinearities in Quantitative Spectral Analysis

REFERENCE: Haaland, D. M., "**Methods to Include Beer's Law Nonlinearities in Quantitative Spectral Analysis,**" *Computerized Quantitative Infrared Analysis, ASTM STP 934*, G. L. M^{C}Clure, Ed., American Society for Testing and Materials, Philadelphia, 1987, pp. 78–94.

ABSTRACT: Multivariate least-squares methods have been recently applied to the quantitative infrared analysis of multicomponent samples. Many deviations from Beer's law can be approximated in linear least-squares analyses by using a calibration set which consists of spectra of known mixtures and by adding a nonzero intercept to Beer's law. More recently, methods which specifically include nonlinear terms in the relationship between concentration and absorbance have been applied to samples whose spectra exhibit Beer's law deviations. Using these methods, reductions in relative errors have been achieved for several nonlinear systems compared to the results of least-squares methods which include only the linear terms. An alternate method to improve the quantitative accuracy in the presence of Beer's law deviations involves using full-spectrum residuals. Since the multivariate least-squares analysis generates estimated pure-component spectra from a calibration set of known mixture spectra, residual spectra can be generated by subtracting the appropriate amounts of the estimated spectra from the known mixture spectra. The residual spectra, which represent the nonlinearities from Beer's law that are not accurately approximated in the multivariate least-squares analysis, are then used as additional terms to improve the least-squares fit of the unknown sample spectrum. Empirically this method has been also found to improve relative errors. These methods have been applied to two systems which exhibit nonlinear Beer's law behavior, that is, binary mixtures of esters and low-resolution gas-phase spectra of nitrous oxide (N_2O) in nitrogen (N_2). Demonstration of the methods and a comparison of the accuracies of the different techniques are made for these two systems.

KEY WORDS: multivariate least-squares analysis, Beer's law deviations, quantitative infrared

It is obvious from the variety and quality of papers presented during this symposium that the use of infrared (IR) spectroscopy is rapidly gaining respectability as a quantitative tool. Earlier difficulties in using optical null spectrometers for quantitative analyses have been largely eliminated with

[1] Member of the technical staff, Sandia National Laboratories, Albuquerque, NM 87185.

the advent of computerized ratio-recording dispersive spectrometers and Fourier transform infrared (FT-IR) spectrometers. The great advantage in speed that IR spectroscopy has over many other methods of quantitative analysis will greatly increase its popularity in the future. However, in order for IR spectroscopy to realize its full potential as a quantitative tool, it must be capable of handling problems encountered in many real samples, for example, the presence of nonlinearities in the relation between absorbance and concentration. We have been applying and testing a variety of methods which either minimize the effects of nonlinearities or actually model the nonlinearities which are present.

The methods we have developed involve full-spectrum, classical multivariate least-squares methods for the quantitative analysis of multicomponent samples [1–5]. We choose to apply full-spectrum least-squares methods because they have the advantage of greater precision and most often exhibit greater accuracy when compared to least-squares methods which limit the frequencies used in the analysis [6–9]. They also offer significantly greater ability to handle severe overlap of spectral features of the sample components. These advantages coupled with least-squares fitting of spectral baselines allow analyses to be performed even when the signal-to-noise ratios are less than 1 [1]. In addition, the use of these methods allows full-spectrum residuals to be calculated, and these can be used to determine the magnitude of nonlinearities, the vibrations affected by nonlinearities, and the presence or even identification of unexpected components [3,10].

We have incorporated a variety of statistical methods to improve the analyses in the presence of Beer's law deviations. Several of these have been described in more detail elsewhere [1–3]. First, we perform the quantitative analysis separately on each spectral peak of the unknown sample spectrum and pool the results for each peak in a statistically efficient manner. The pooling is a weighted average of each component concentration where the weighting factors are inversely proportional to the estimated variances for each component in each peak. This means that those peaks which are fit best (including the linear baseline under each peak) are given the greatest weight in the analysis. Therefore, if only a portion of the spectrum follows Beer's law, this portion will be given greater importance in the analysis relative to those bands which do not follow Beer's law. This is also an effective method for minimizing the effect of unexpected components in the unknown samples [2]. Second, we have applied multivariate least-squares methods which allow the use of known mixtures in the analysis and at the same time provide for a nonzero intercept to be added to Beer's law. Since the mixtures contain the molecular interactions and other nonlinearities present in the system, using them as a calibration set allows the best least-squares linear estimate of the nonlinearities over the concentration range spanned by the calibration standards. Third, after an initial analysis of the unknown using all the calibration standards, the concentration range of the calibration set can be reduced to more closely surround the component concentrations of the unknown. In this manner, the nonlinearities will be better approximated since their linear approximation is more accurate over the narrower concentration range. These three methods have been implemented and have been presented elsewhere [3]. They serve to minimize the effects of nonlinearities.

However, we are not restricted to assuming a linear Beer's law model in our calibration. We can actually assume a nonlinear model with additional terms representing quadratic, cross-product and higher order terms. Alternatively, we can include in the analysis the full-spectrum residuals which can be obtained from the calibration set after completing the multivariate least-squares analysis. These are the remaining nonlinearities and noise that are not normally included in the analysis. If some or all of the linearly independent residuals are included in the analysis as separate components, these become additional parameters to improve the least-squares curve fitting. If these residuals model real and reproducible nonlinearities in the system, then more accurate results should be expected when these residuals are included in the analysis.

Theory

In order to describe the nonlinear methods in more detail, a brief outline of our previously published multivariate least-squares methods [3] will be presented. The analysis of the unknown actually requires two least-squares steps. The first is the calibration phase where pure-component spectra are estimated by least-squares techniques from the spectra of a series of known mixture calibration standards. The estimated spectra are then used in the least-squares analysis of the unknown sample spectrum.

Initially we assume that Beer's law is valid

$$A = abc \tag{1}$$

where

A = absorbance at a given frequency,
a = absorptivity,
b = pathlength, and
c = concentration.

For a multicomponent sample we have at each frequency i in the spectrum

$$A_i = \sum_{j=1}^{l} k_{ij}c_j + e_i \tag{2}$$

where the k_{ij} terms represent the product of the pathlength and the absorptivity for component j at frequency i. The e_i terms are the random error in the measured spectrum. The error is assumed to be normally distributed with an expectation of zero. The full spectrum then yields a series of n equations where n is the number of frequencies. These may be put into matrix form

$$A = KC + E \qquad (3)$$

where

A = the $n \times m$ matrix whose columns represent the spectrum of each of the m standard mixtures,

K = the $n \times l$ matrix whose columns represent the l pure-component spectra at unit concentration and unit relative path length,

C = the $l \times m$ matrix of the known component concentrations, and

E = the $n \times m$ matrix of random measurement errors in the spectra.

The least-squares estimate of the matrix of pure-component spectra $\hat{K}$ is given by

$$\hat{K} = AC'(CC')^{-1} \qquad (4)$$

where the primes indicate transposed matrices and the $^{-1}$ represents the inverse of the matrix. This is the simplest solution. We have implemented a weighted least-squares solution which includes a nonzero intercept on Beer's law and accommodates variations in sample pathlengths [3]. The matrix to be inverted in Eq 4 is a small $l \times l$ matrix, and this inversion is performed readily with the computer. Therefore, as many frequencies as desired can be added without increasing the size of the matrix to be inverted which is in contrast with other methods [6,7].

Deviations from Beer's law can be modeled by adding terms to Eq 2 which are nonlinear in concentration. For example, if we choose to add a quadratic term, then Eq 2 becomes

$$A_i = \sum_{j=1}^{l} (k_{ij}c_j + k'_{ij}c_j^2) + e_i \qquad (5)$$

Then the matrix equations become

$$
\begin{vmatrix} A_{11} \cdots A_{1m} \\ \vdots \qquad \vdots \\ \vdots \qquad \vdots \\ \vdots \qquad \vdots \\ A_{n1} \cdots A_{nm} \end{vmatrix}
=
\begin{vmatrix} k_{11}\, k'_{11} \cdots k_{1l}\, k'_{1l} \\ \vdots \qquad \qquad \vdots \\ \vdots \qquad \qquad \vdots \\ \vdots \qquad \qquad \vdots \\ k_{n1}\, k'_{n1} \cdots k_{nl}\, k'_{nl} \end{vmatrix}
\begin{vmatrix} c_{11} \cdots c_{1m} \\ c_{11}^2 \cdots c_{1m}^2 \\ \vdots \qquad \vdots \\ c_{l1} \cdots c_{lm} \\ c_{l1}^2 \cdots c_{lm}^2 \end{vmatrix}
+
\begin{vmatrix} e_{11} \cdots e_{1m} \\ \vdots \qquad \vdots \\ \vdots \qquad \vdots \\ \vdots \qquad \vdots \\ e_{n1} \cdots e_{nm} \end{vmatrix} \qquad (6)
$$

or

$$A = \underline{KC} + E \tag{7}$$

where the bars under the matrices indicate the matrices that are augmented by the quadratic correction terms k'_{ij} or $c_{jk}{}^2$. The primed columns of $\underline{K}$ then represent the full-spectrum quadratic correction terms to the linear model. Equation 7 still allows a linear least-squares solution since the absorbance is linear in both the concentration and the squared concentration terms. The least-squares solution is then

$$\hat{\underline{K}} = A\underline{C}'(\underline{CC}')^{-1} \tag{8}$$

Similar methods are used to introduce cross-product terms and higher-order terms if desired. Previously, inverse (or P-matrix) least-squares methods have used models nonlinear in absorbance [9]. However, the inverse methods are limited in the number of frequencies which may be included in the analysis, and they may exhibit other problems which are outlined in Ref 11.

In the analysis of an unknown sample, we perform a least-squares fit of the sample spectrum using the least-squares estimates of the pure-component spectra which were generated in the calibration phase. This prediction phase then results in the estimate of the sample concentrations. For the Beer's law model, we have

$$\begin{vmatrix} A_1{}^s \\ \vdots \\ A_n{}^s \end{vmatrix} = \begin{vmatrix} \hat{k}_{11} \cdots \hat{k}_{1l} \\ \vdots \quad\quad \vdots \\ \hat{k}_{n1} \cdots \hat{k}_{nl} \end{vmatrix} \begin{vmatrix} c_1 \\ \vdots \\ c_l \end{vmatrix} + \begin{vmatrix} e_1 \\ \vdots \\ e_n \end{vmatrix} \tag{9}$$

or

$$A^s = \hat{K}C + E \tag{10}$$

where the A^s vector represents the unknown sample spectrum, the $\hat{K}$-matrix is determined from Eq 4 and the C-vector is composed of the unknown sample component concentrations. The least-squares solution for C is given by

$$\hat{C} = (\hat{K}'\hat{K})^{-1}\hat{K}'A^s \tag{11}$$

This is the simplest solution. In fact, we implement a weighted least-squares solution and include a least-squares fit of a linear baseline under each spectral peak [3]. The analysis is performed separately for each peak, and the results are pooled inversely proportional to the estimated variances to give the advantages described earlier. Again the matrix to be inverted in

Eq 11 is $l \times l$ independent of the number of frequencies included in the analysis.

If the quadratic model was used in the calibration, then technically we should perform a nonlinear least-squares analysis during prediction since the c_j and c_j^2 terms are not independent in the model. However, the purpose of this initial study was to use the existing software which is now in the public domain. Therefore, the c_j^2 or other nonlinear concentration terms are treated separately in the analysis of the unknown sample spectrum. They are used to improve the curve fitting by introducing nonlinear correction terms, but the analysis can be based solely on the estimated linear concentrations. Alternatively, a weighted average or pooling of the estimates of the linear and nonlinear concentration terms can be used in the calculation of the concentrations. Again the weighting factors are inversely proportional to the estimated variances. The variance of the estimate of squared concentrations or other nonlinear terms can be obtained with minor modifications of the current software. For the quadratic model, the linear least-squares solution for concentration terms is simply

$$\hat{\underline{C}} = (\hat{\underline{K}}'\hat{\underline{K}})^{-1}\hat{\underline{K}}'A^s \tag{12}$$

where the $\hat{\underline{C}}$ and $\hat{\underline{K}}$ matrices are the least-squares estimates of the augmented matrices as exhibited in Eq 6.

Full-spectrum residuals can be also included in the least-squares fitting of unknown sample spectra. These residuals represent those portions of the calibration mixture spectra which are not modeled in the estimated pure-component spectra. Therefore, nonlinearities which are not accurately approximated in the multivariate least-squares analysis will be present in the residual spectra. A different residual can be calculated from each standard mixture spectrum. The value of the residual (r_{im}) at each frequency i for calibration spectrum m can be calculated as follows

$$r_{im} = A_{im} - \frac{1}{b_m} \sum_{j=1}^{l} \hat{k}_{ij}c_{jm} \tag{13}$$

where

A_{im} = absorbance of the mth calibration mixture at frequency i,
b_m = pathlength for mixture m,
$\hat{k}_{ij}$ = least-squares estimate of the k_{ij} term, and
c_{jm} = concentration of the jth component in mixture m.

The number of linearly independent full-spectrum residuals which can be generated is $(m - l)$ where m is the number of standard mixtures and l is the number of components. Choosing only those residuals which have important nonzero components can reduce potential problems. For instance, overfitting can result if the residuals model noise or errors that are representative only of the calibration spectra and not of the unknown sample spectra. If residuals are used in the analysis, care should be exercised since the system can become underdetermined in the absence of nonlinearities, and the resulting residuals would be only random noise with no new spectral information. The best method to avoid these problems would be to apply principle components analysis to the residual spectra in order to determine those orthogonal components which are significantly above the noise and which should be included for improved prediction of concentrations in unknown samples.

Experimental Procedures

The experimental procedures have been detailed elsewhere [3]. Briefly, binary mixtures of two esters (ethylhexanoate and cyclohexyl acetate) were mixed by weight (~0.5% relative accuracy) and placed in a 20 μm pathlength sealed cell. The ester spectra were obtained at 2 cm^{-1} resolution with a Nicolet 7199 spectrometer equipped with a mercury-cadmium-tellurium (Hg-Cd-Te) detector. The gas-phase nitrous oxide (N_2O) spectra at a total pressure of 640 torr were measured in 2-cm pathlength cells using sapphire windows. The various samples were obtained as certified standards in nitrogen (N_2) diluent gas or were prepared from pure N_2O diluted by N_2. These latter samples were then analyzed by gas chromatographic methods. An InSb detector was used to obtain 0.5 cm^{-1} resolution spectra. The least-squares quantitative analysis computer program, which is in the public domain, was written in FORTRAN 77 and is part of the Nicolet Users Library.

Results and Discussion

The measured pure component spectra of the two esters are presented in Fig. 1. They exhibit a high degree of spectral overlap which makes quantitative analysis difficult if the analysis is restricted to a small number of analytical frequencies. However, the application of the full-spectrum least-squares methods used here can significantly improve the quantitative results for this highly overlapped system. The two pure-component spectra and the spectra of six binary mixtures of the two esters were used in the analysis. The six mixtures varied in relative mole fraction from 1:3 to 3:1. Either the pure-component spectra or three mixtures at 1:3, 1:1, and 3:1 relative mole fractions were used as the reference set in the analyses. The methods were then tested on a validation set of three separate mixtures at 3:2, 1:1, and 2:3 relative mole fractions.

Figure 2 shows the measured pure ethyl hexanoate spectrum and that estimated by multivariate least-squares methods using the calibration set containing three mixtures. Similar plots for the cyclohexyl acetate component can be also obtained. The lower spectrum in Fig. 2 is the difference

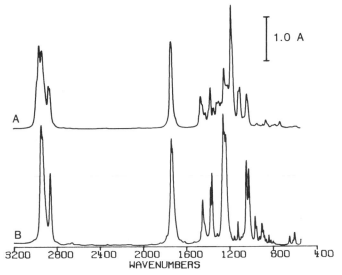

FIG. 1—*Infrared spectra of* (A) *ethyl hexanoate and* (B) *cyclohexyl acetate in a 20* μm *liquid cell.* [*From Ref 3.*]

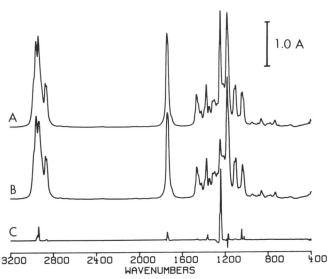

FIG. 2—(A) *Ethyl hexanoate spectrum estimated from weighted multivariate least-squares analysis of 3 mixtures of the two esters.* (B) *Measured spectrum of pure ethyl hexanoate.* (C) *Spectrum A minus spectrum B.* [*In part from Ref 3.*]

between the measured and estimated spectra. This residual spectrum should be random noise if Beer's law is followed throughout the spectrum. The deviations from zero in the residual spectrum yield valuable qualitative information. They indicate which spectral frequencies or molecular vibrations are nonlinear. These nonlinearities may be due to molecular interactions, spectrometer nonlinearities, or dispersion in refractive index of the samples. The latter two may be separated from the first by performing studies as a function of pathlength. Molecular interactions are unaffected by pathlength variations while spectrometer nonlinearities and effects due to dispersion in refractive index are greatly affected by pathlength.

In the case of the mixture of esters, we find that the nonlinearities are primarily due to spectrometer nonlinearities [3] as might be expected by the presence of highly absorbing bands. In any case, Fig. 2 shows clearly that this set of mixtures exhibits some significant Beer's law nonlinearities. However, since the least-squares estimated spectra are obtained from mixtures already containing some of these nonlinearities, more accurate results are expected and are obtained when spectra estimated from mixtures are used in the analysis of unknown sample spectra. This can be demonstrated graphically as shown in Fig. 3. The first spectrum in Fig. 3 is that measured for the 1:1 calibration mixture of the two esters. The lower two spectra are residuals calculated by subtracting the known proportions of the measured pure-component spectra (middle spectrum in Fig. 3) or estimated pure-component spectra (lower spectrum in Fig. 3). The nonlinearities are much greater using the measured pure-component spectra. Since the estimated pure-component spectra were obtained from known mixtures, the nonlinearities are better approximated to this case as demonstrated by the smaller residuals shown in the lower portion of Fig. 3. This implies that the spectrometer nonlinearities were reproducible. Thus, more accurate results are expected using the multivariate least-squares estimates of the pure-component spectra.

In fact, the residual at the bottom of Fig. 3 can be further reduced if a nonlinear model is assumed in the calibration. Again this implies that more accurate results can be obtained with the nonlinear model. In the case of the esters, we choose to introduce concentration cross-product terms, that is, c_1c_2 terms to model the nonlinearities. As described in Ref 12, an explicit quadratic model cannot be used in binary mixtures where the sum of the mole fractions of the components being analyzed is one. The cross-product term in this case can be shown to include an implied quadratic term.

Alternatively, we can include the nonlinearities by using the lower residual spectrum presented in Fig. 3 as a separate component in the least-squares analysis. As described previously, this residual spectrum represents that portion of the full-spectrum nonlinearities which is not approximated in the Beer's law model multivariate least-squares analysis. By using this residual spectrum as a separate component in the analysis, better curve fitting can

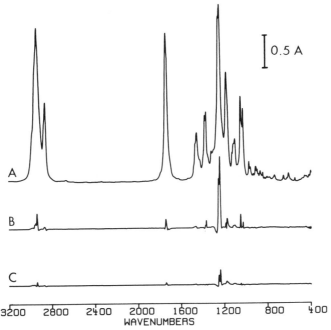

FIG. 3—(A) *Spectrum of 0.559 mole fraction ethyl hexanoate and 0.441 mole fraction cyclohexyl acetate in 20 μm liquid cell. (B) Residual after subtracting 0.559 of the pure ethyl hexanoate spectrum and 0.441 of the pure cyclohexyl acetate spectrum. (C) Residual after subtracting the same proportions of the spectra estimated from three separate mixture spectra. [In part from Ref 3.]*

be achieved, and empirically we find that more accurate results are obtained than using a simple Beer's law model. Use of all the independent residuals is mathematically equivalent to the methods developed by Spragg and Ford [13]. However, the ability to judiciously select the residuals minimizes the problems with overfitting and singular matrices which are possible with the methods developed by Spragg and Ford. Those residuals that are primarily noise or that are not significantly different from other residuals can be eliminated from the analysis.

The results from the least-squares analysis of the esters are presented in Table 1. These results are simply the average of the absolute values of the relative percent errors (referred to as average relative errors in the remainder of the paper) for the three mixtures of esters in the validation set for five different least-squares analyses. The first uses the measured pure-component ester spectra in the analysis of the "unknown" sample spectra. In this case, no least-squares calibration phase is required. The average relative error of 3.8% is actually 3 to 10 times better than was obtained with alternate least-squares software supplied by Nicolet which was limited to a small number of spectral frequencies. This advantage is a result of the following:

TABLE 1—*Summary of least-squares results for ester mixtures.*

Spectra Used for Prediction	Average % Relative Error
Pure components	3.8
Least-squares estimated components	2.4
Estimated components and residual	1.3
Estimated components and cross-products (c_1, c_2, c_1c_2)	1.2
Estimated components (nearest two standards)	0.9

(1) using all frequencies in spectral peaks, (2) performing a weighted least-squares analysis to give greater emphasis to data with higher signal-to-noise ratios, (3) fitting a linear baseline under each spectral peak, and (4) pooling the results for each peak inversely proportional to the estimated variance of each component in each peak.

The second method listed in Table 1 involves a multivariate least-squares calibration using known mixture spectra to obtain estimated pure-component spectra. Since the estimated spectra include the best linear least-squares approximation of the nonlinearities, using them in the analysis of the "unknown" spectra further reduces the average relative error.

The third least-squares method involves the inclusion of the residual shown at the bottom of Fig. 3 as a separate component in the analysis along with the two estimated pure-component spectra. Again a reduction in average relative error is noted. The fourth method includes the concentration cross product as well as the linear concentration terms in the analysis. Thus, a nonlinear interaction term has been included in the model during calibration and prediction. Using the estimates of only the linear concentration terms during the least-squares prediction phase of the unknown spectra yields the fourth average relative error presented in Table 1.

Finally, the last method presented in Table 1 involves a simple narrowing of the concentration range used in the calibration. This is accomplished by taking the analyses of any of the four preceding methods to yield initial concentration values. Then the two references closest in concentration to the initially calculated concentrations are used in the least-squares calibration. The resulting estimated spectra more closely matched the nonlinearities of each unknown sample because the concentration range over which the nonlinearities were approximated was reduced. However, this latter method must be used with caution since errors and noise in either the calibration spectra or concentrations can be magnified by this procedure and the matrices to be inverted approach singularity as the concentrations of the calibration samples come closer to being identical.

Since the calibration and validation sets of ester mixtures each contain only three samples, the ranking of the average relative errors of the last three results in Table 1 may not be the same for a large population of unknowns. In addition, the relative accuracy of each method may vary from system to system. Therefore, each new system which varies in chemical composition or concentration range must be evaluated separately to determine which least-squares method will give the most accurate results.

In addition to the analysis of liquid esters, we performed a quantitative analysis of gas-phase N_2O in a background of N_2 at 640 torr total pressure. This system exhibits much greater nonlinearities than the ester mixtures due to the large concentration range studied and the relatively low resolution used in obtaining the spectra. Although the natural line widths of N_2O at 640 torr are ~0.12 cm^{-1}, 0.5 cm^{-1} resolution was used to reduce data collection times, data storage requirements, and noise levels. However, this low resolution results in deviations from Beer's law [14].

Figure 4 shows the spectrum of 14.7% N_2O in N_2 over the spectral range of interest using the InSb detector. The major rotational-vibrational band centered at ~2200 cm^{-1} was initially used in the analysis since this band offers the greatest sensitivity to low concentrations. Figure 5A shows this same band at a different scale expansion in both absorbance and wavenumber. The spectrum in Fig. 5B is that of N_2O at ~1/40 the concentration of the first sample. It has been scale expanded by a factor of 40 to compensate for the concentration differences. If Beer's law were followed, spectra A and B in Fig. 5 should exhibit identical intensities and shapes. However, neither the shape nor the intensities are the same for these two spectra. The lowest spectrum in Fig. 5 is the difference between spectra A and B. This

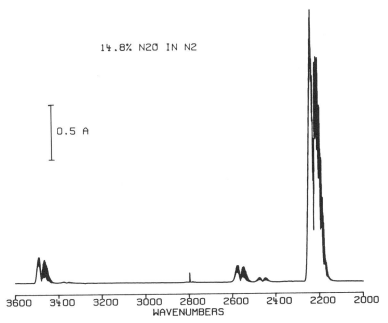

FIG. 4—*Spectrum of 14.8% N_2O in N_2 at 640 torr total pressure in a 2 cm pathlength cell.*

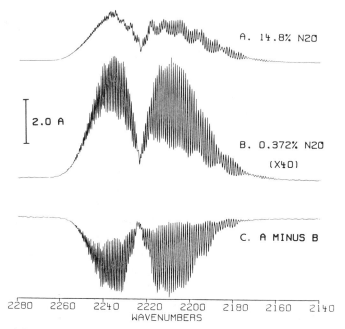

FIG. 5—(A) *Spectrum of 14.8% N_2O in N_2 at 640 torr.* (B) *Spectrum of 0.372% N_2O in N_2 at 640 torr (scale expanded by a factor of 40 relative to* (A). (C) *Spectrum* A *minus spectrum* B.

residual should be zero if Beer's law were valid. The large intensity of the residual is an indication of the severity of the Beer's law deviations. In fact, if either spectrum were used as a single reference in the analysis of the other, the calculated concentrations would be in error by a factor of 2.5.

The concentrations of the N_2O samples in the calibration and validation sets are presented in Table 2. The calibration set covers a concentration range of 40 while the range of the validation set is almost 500. Normally the concentrations used in the validation set should lie within the range of the calibration set since extrapolations outside this range tend to be less accurate. However, the low signal-to-noise level of the 0.035% sample in the validation set made it inappropriate to use as a calibration standard.

TABLE 2—*N_2O sample concentrations in 640 torr N_2.*

Calibration Set, %	Validation Set, %
0.372	0.035
0.960	0.367
1.97	7.53
6.94	15.1
14.8	

Since we know that the system is highly nonlinear, we can assume a nonlinear calibration model using terms linear in concentration and linear in the square of the concentration. The results of a multivariate least-squares calibration using the five calibration standards yields the estimated spectra presented in Fig. 6. The upper spectrum represents the estimated linear concentration term and the lower spectrum is that for the full-spectrum quadratic correction term, each at one percent concentration. The quadratic term is negative throughout the spectrum. It is expected to be negative since the measured absorbance at any concentration is less than would be expected based on a Beer's law model. It is important to note that Fig. 6 represents the estimated spectra at the one percent level. At 10%, the linear term increases by a factor of 10 while the quadratic term increases by 100 fold. Therefore, the quadratic correction term becomes more significant at higher concentrations. However, the quadratic term is negligible at very low concentrations (that is, Beer's law is quite accurate at low concentration).

Table 3 shows the results of four different multivariate least-squares analyses applied to the N_2O validation set. Again the results are presented as the average of the absolute value of the percent relative errors. The first three involve the use of only the major band centered at ~ 2200 cm^{-1} while the fourth uses only the four minor bands shown in Fig. 4. The multivariate least-squares analysis using the linear Beer's law model yields an average

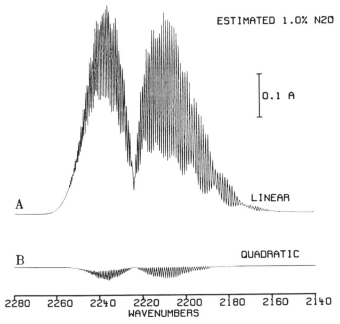

FIG. 6—(A) *Least-squares estimated N_2O spectrum; linear concentration at 1% concentration.* (B) *Least-squares estimated N_2O spectrum; quadratic concentration at 1% concentration.*

TABLE 3—*Summary of least-squares results for N_2O samples.*

Spectra Used for Prediction	Average % Relative Error
Estimated major N_2O band (linear)	26.0
Estimated major N_2O band (linear + four residuals)	18.0
Estimated major N_2O band (linear + quadratic)	7.7
Estimated minor N_2O bands (linear)	1.3

relative error of 26%. This is a significant improvement over using any single sample in the calibration set as a reference standard in the least-squares analysis of the validation samples. This latter method yielded average relative errors of 44 to 106% depending on which sample was used as the standard.

The second method listed in Table 3 uses the estimated spectra which were determined during the calibration of the first method. However, four of the residuals obtained from the calibration spectra were also included in the analysis as separate components in addition to the least-squares estimated pure spectra. By this procedure the nonlinearities not included in the estimated spectrum are included during the analysis of the "unknown" validation set. If the residuals accurately model the nonlinearities of the unknown, then more accurate curve fitting can be achieved and more accurate results should be obtained. Table 3 demonstrates that this method does, in fact, yield higher accuracies for the N_2O in N_2 mixtures than the linear multivariate least-squares analysis.

The third method listed in Table 3 involves the introduction of a nonlinear model during the calibration phase. In this case, both linear and quadratic terms were used during calibration. The estimated spectra used in the analysis of the "unknown" validation spectra are those presented in Fig. 6. The use of both linear and quadratic terms in the analysis further reduces the average relative error. In this case, the results of both the linear and quadratic terms were included in the estimation of the sample concentrations by pooling the results inversely proportional to the estimated variances for each term. The resulting average relative error is significantly better than possible by the more simple linear multivariate least-squares analysis applied to the same data.

The preceding analyses were all performed using the major infrared band of N_2O since it provides the greatest sensitivity for the analysis. However, as demonstrated previously, the nonlinearities in this band are quite significant over the concentration range studied. The four minor N_2O infrared bands observed in Fig. 4 are at least an order of magnitude less intense than the 2200 cm^{-1} band at the 14.7% N_2O concentration level. Because of the nonlinearities in the 2200 cm^{-1} band, the minor bands are actually a factor of 25 less intense than the major band in the 0.035% N_2O sample spectrum. In fact, the maximum signal-to-noise ratio (S/N) for this latter spectrum is less than or equal to one at any frequency in the region of the minor bands. The maximum S/N is 10 in the 0.367% N_2O sample over the same spectral range. For these reasons the minor bands were originally excluded from the analysis. However, a linear multivariate least-squares analysis applied to the four minor bands results in a very small 1.3% relative error as shown in Table 3. This result demonstrates three important points. First, the minor bands must be quite linear over the nearly 500 fold concentration range present in the validation samples. Second, this demonstrates the ability of nearly full-spectrum least-squares methods (1800 frequencies were included in this latter analysis) to accurately monitor concentrations down to the noise level when baseline fitting is also included. Finally, it is clear that when nonlinearities are present, a thorough analysis of the calibration and validation sample spectra should be made in order to achieve the best possible method for quantitative analysis of the samples.

Summary

We have shown that there are a variety of methods that can be used to quantitatively analyze samples whose infrared spectra do not follow Beer's law. In addition to methods described previously for full-spectrum multivariate least-squares techniques, nonlinear models (cross-products, quadratics, and higher order terms) can now be included in the analysis of the calibration and unknown spectra. Thus we are not restricted to linear approximations of nonlinear data, and greater accuracies are achieved. Inclusion of spectral residuals is an alternative method that can be used to more accurately model nonlinearities. These residuals improve the curve fitting when nonlinearities are present, and empirically we find that accuracies are improved.

However, caution should be always exercised when deviations from Beer's law are present. As demonstrated in the case of the N_2O samples, the best method to apply is not always intuitively obvious. Each available method should be carefully tested using adequately large calibration and validation sets in order to properly choose the best method of quantitative analysis for each chemical system studied.

Acknowledgments

The author would like to acknowledge the aid of M. C. Oborny in collecting the infrared spectra. Dr. R. G. Easterling provided statistical consulting for the new nonlinear methods, and D. A. Vopicka helped write the Fortran programs used in these analyses.

This work was performed at Sandia National Laboratories supported by the U.S. Department of Energy under Contract Number DE-AC04-DP00789.

References

[1] Haaland, D. M. and Easterling, R. G., *Applied Spectroscopy,* Vol. 34, 1980, p. 539.

[2] Haaland, D. M. and Easterling, R. G., *Applied Spectroscopy,* Vol. 36, 1982, p. 665.

[3] Haaland, D. M., Easterling, R. G., and Vopicka, D. A., *Applied Spectroscopy,* Vol. 39, 1985, p. 73.

[4] Antoon, M. K., Koenig, J. H., and Koenig, J. L., *Applied Spectroscopy,* Vol. 31, 1977, p. 518.

[5] Tyson, L. L., Ling, Y.-C., and Mann, C. K., *Applied Spectroscopy,* Vol. 38, 1984, p. 663.

[6] Brown, C. W., Lynch, P. F., Obremski, R. J., and Lavery, D. S., *Analytical Chemistry,* Vol. 54, 1982, p. 1472.

[7] Kisner, H. J., Brown, C. W., and Kavarnos, G. J., *Analytical Chemistry,* Vol. 55, 1983, p. 1703.

[8] Bartick, E. G., Corbett, J. C., and McClure, G. L., ACS Symposium Series, V. 1982, No. 197, 1982, p. 185.

[9] Maris, M. A., Brown, C. W., and Lavery, D. S., *Analytical Chemistry,* Vol. 55, 1983, p. 1694.

[10] Haaland, D. M. and Barbour, R. L., *American Laboratory,* Vol. 17, No. 7, 1985, p. 14.

[11] Haaland, D. M., *1985 International Conference on Fourier and Computerized Infrared Spectroscopy,* J. G. Grasselli and D. G. Cameron, Eds., Proceedings SPIE, Vol. 553, 1985, p. 241.

[12] Cornell, J. A., *Experiments With Mixtures: Designs, Models, and the Analysis of Mixture Data,* John Wiley and Sons, NY, 1981.

[13] Spragg, R. A. and Ford, M. A., "Multicomponent Quantitative IR Analysis by Curve Fitting of Discrete Frequency Measurements," Paper 407 presented at the Pittsburgh Conference and Exposition on Analytical Chemistry and Applied Spectroscopy, Atlantic City, NJ, 5–9 March 1984.

[14] Ramsey, D. A., *Journal of the American Chemical Society,* Vol. 74, No. 72, 1952.

Richard A. Crocombe,[1] Mark L. Olson,[1] and Stephen L. Hill[1]

Quantitative Fourier Transform Infrared Methods for Real Complex Samples

REFERENCE: Crocombe, R. A., Olson, M. L., and Hill, S. L., "**Quantitative Fourier Transform Infrared Methods for Real Complex Samples,**" *Computerized Quantitative Infrared Analysis, ASTM STP 934,* G. L. MᶜClure, Ed., American Society for Testing and Materials, Philadelphia, 1987, pp. 95–130.

ABSTRACT: Quantitative analysis for one-component systems (for example, additives in polymers, dilute solutions) is well understood, and the mathematical methods needed are comparatively simple. In recent years, software for multicomponent analysis has been made available for Fourier transform infrared (FT-IR) instruments, and two methods are commonly employed, termed **K**-matrix and **P**-matrix. Although the mathematical techniques involved have been described, their practical application is less well documented, and there are a number of pitfalls for the unwary analyst. This paper describes some of those pitfalls, and methods for avoiding them. Of great concern is the common occurrence of calibration using carefully prepared standards, followed by the analysis of real samples that contain impurities. This can have disastrous consequences no matter how good the calibration is. The range of concentrations that a multicomponent analysis actually spans, in reality, can be far less than the analyst may think at first sight. Some examples of applications of multicomponent infrared analysis are given, including extensions to the use of newer techniques such as diffuse reflectance, photoacoustic spectroscopy and microscopy.

KEY WORDS: infrared spectrometry, quantitative analysis, computer applications, matrix methods, Fourier transform infrared spectrometry

Quantitative infrared analysis is based upon the application of the Bouger-Beer-Lambert law, commonly referred to as Beer's law. The principles of infrared (IR) analysis are described in several standard texts [1–5], with emphasis upon single component systems, and the application of Beer's law to multicomponent systems has also been well described [5,6], but the inherent mathematical complexities have historically limited routine use to the simple case. The key features of multicomponent analysis include the ability to perform quantitative analysis on systems with overlapping bands; to calibrate using mixtures, therefore allowing for interactions between components; and to overdetermine analyses using more spectral data and standards than the minimum mathematically required.

---

[1] FT-IR product manager, applications software manager, and applications chemist, respectively, Bio-Rad Laboratories, Digilab Division, Cambridge, MA 02139.

There has been increased interest in multicomponent analyses recently, principally due to the availability of the mathematical routines required on computer-based infrared spectrometers. Typically, a commercial quantitative software package will abstract the absorbance values required from the spectra of calibration and analytical samples, calculate the matrix of calibration factors, and print out concentration data for the unknown samples. This allows automation of IR analysis, as well as ending the burden of inverting matrices by hand [5], or the problem of transferring data to a separate computer. The slow and error-prone step of measuring peak heights by hand from hard-copy spectra is also eliminated.

Quantitative infrared analyses in common use all assume Beer's law, implicitly or otherwise; some nonlinear approaches have been described in the literature [7,8], but will not be discussed here. Four broad types of algorithm have been used: simple applications (single component) of Beer's law; matrix applications (multicomponent) of Beer's law; spectral fitting; and spectral search methods.

The simple applications typically use peak heights or peak areas, and a graph of concentration versus absorbance is plotted, or a linear least squares regression performed. Two types of matrix manipulation have been described, termed **K**-matrix [6] and **P**-matrix [7,8]. Spectral fitting approaches, described by Antoon, Koenig, and Koenig [9] and Haaland and Easterling [10], typically fit spectra of pure components to those of mixture spectra, and extensions, using for instance, factor analysis techniques, allow the abstraction of spectra of chemically inaccessible species [11,12]. Last, spectral search methods [13,14] treat absorbance spectral data points as a normalized n-dimensional vector, and compute a degree of "likeness" based upon vector dot products. Because of the mathematical procedure used, this approach is sometimes called a vector method, although others have used this term to describe manipulations in interferogram space. This dot product approach is also used in screening algorithms.

In this paper we explore in detail the application of **K**- and **P**-matrix methods, highlighting important practical details, and giving some examples. As techniques make the transition from research tools to everyday use, many pitfalls and subtleties become apparent, which this paper seeks to illuminate. We also indicate possible extensions to these methods, applications to systems where Beer's law, in its purest form, is not valid.

Theory

Fundamentals

Beer's law [1-5] relates absorbance to quantity of material and sample pathlength and is stated here for the simple case of a single compound at a single frequency

$$A = abc \qquad (1)$$

where

A = absorbance at a frequency,
a = absorbtivity of the compound at that frequency,
b = pathlength of the sample, and
c = concentration of the compound in the sample.

A typical quantitative analysis has two distinct parts: a calibration step and an analysis step. For the calibration step, standards are made up with different but known concentrations of a species. The spectra of these standards are recorded under similar conditions, and the absorbance at a frequency measured for each standard. Thus A is measured, while b and c are known. Then a may be calculated. In the analysis step, the spectrum of a sample with an unknown concentration of that species is measured. In this case, A (the absorbance at the frequency used in the calibration) is measured, b is known, a has been determined in the calibration step, and c, the concentration of the species in the sample, can be obtained.

In this simple case only one measurement is theoretically needed to determine a. However, it is good practice to run several standards and then to perform a least-squares regression to calculate a. This is known as overdetermination—more data is used than is strictly necessary. Overdetermination tends to reduce the effect of random errors and allows the detection of systematic errors.

Most of the quantitative literature describes the calibration step in great detail, and barely mentions the analysis step. This is because more expertise is usually required in setting up the calibration—choosing bands, selecting the sampling technique, etc.—and any errors made here will affect all analyses. Once the analysis is calibrated, the actual analysis of unknowns is relatively straightforward, and the operator need not know any of the details of the band or algorithm selection but merely needs to follow the sample preparation and measurement instructions closely. The actual mathematics of the analysis step can be quite automatic.

The *K*-Matrix Approach

Very few systems having practical application actually contain only one component. Therefore Beer's law has to be formulated to accommodate many components and appropriate mathematical methods used to deal with the resulting complexities, but the general scheme described previously is still true. Because more than one component may be present in every sample, absorbance measurements must be made at more than one frequency (for every calibration sample, and, of course, in the unknowns) in order to determine these different components. In practical cases an absorbance measurement may be an absolute absorbance, an absorbance relative to a local baseline, or an integrated absorbance, the area under the absorbance curve between two frequencies, perhaps also relative to a local baseline. In multicomponent determinations it is perfectly permissible to use several of these types of "absorbance measurements" within a single analysis.

In a multicomponent system Beer's law is additive, and in the discussion that follows a and b are combined into a single constant k. Thus the absorbance at a single frequency is equal to the sum of kc terms for each component

$$k = ab \tag{2}$$

and

$$A = kc \tag{3}$$

Therefore

$$A = k_1 c_1 + k_2 c_2 + k_3 c_3 \ldots k_n c_n \tag{4}$$

This can be generalized if many frequencies are considered, and a series of equations generated

$$
\begin{aligned}
A_1 &= k_{11} c_1 + k_{12} c_2 + \ldots k_{1n} c_n \\
A_2 &= k_{21} c_1 + k_{22} c_2 + \ldots k_{2n} c_n \\
&\vdots \qquad \vdots \qquad \vdots \qquad \qquad \vdots \\
A_n &= k_{n1} c_1 + k_{n2} c_2 + \ldots k_{nn} c_n
\end{aligned}
\tag{5}
$$

These equations can be expressed in the more compact matrix notation

$$
\begin{bmatrix} A_1 \\ A_2 \\ \vdots \\ A_n \end{bmatrix}
=
\begin{bmatrix} k_{11}\, k_{12} \ldots k_{1n} \\ k_{21}\, k_{22} \ldots k_{2n} \\ \vdots \\ k_{n1}\, k_{n2} \ldots k_{nn} \end{bmatrix}
*
\begin{bmatrix} c_1 \\ c_2 \\ \vdots \\ c_n \end{bmatrix}
\tag{6}
$$

or

$$\mathbf{A} = \mathbf{KC} \tag{7}$$

In the calibration step the matrix of absorbances, $\mathbf{A}$, (that is, absorbances at several frequencies in all of the spectra of samples used for calibration) is found by experiment, the concentrations are known, $\mathbf{K}$ can be calculated. Because $\mathbf{C}$ is not usually square, each side of the equation is multiplied by the transpose of $\mathbf{C}$

$$\mathbf{AC}^t = \mathbf{KCC}^t \tag{8}$$

CC^t is square and invertable, so both sides can be multiplied by $(CC^t)^{-1}$, resulting in

$$K = AC^t(CC^t)^{-1} \qquad (9)$$

K is the least squares fit between the observed and calculated absorbances and is called the training or calibration matrix. In the analysis step the absorbances, A, of the unknown sample at those same frequencies are measured, and the concentrations of the components are then calculated

$$C = (K^tK)^{-1}K^tA \qquad (10)$$

C is the matrix of desired concentration data, the concentrations of the various components in the unknown sample. The solution is done in this manner, rather than directly inverting C and K, because these matrices will only be square if no overdetermination is done. Further mathematical details are discussed by Bauman [5] and Brown [6].

It should be noted here that the concentration data does not have to be arranged to match the order in which absorbance data is abstracted from the spectra; information from all spectral frequencies is used for all components. The matrix does not have to be presented with the information that component A absorbs at a certain frequency; these correlations are calculated. If one sample is analyzed at a time then C and A are one dimensional matrices in the analytical step. Many samples could be analyzed simultaneously, however, in which case C and A would be rectangular.

Back-Calculation of Original Concentrations

In the calibration step, once K has been determined, it is common practice to back-calculate the concentrations of the standards, using the K-matrix. In an exactly determined case these back-calculated values will be exactly those that were input. In sample-overdetermined cases, however, because the equivalent of a least-squares regression has been performed, this will no longer be the case. A degree of overdetermination empirically found to be satisfactory in most cases is to use twice the minimum number of samples required. (However, see the following sections that discuss the importance of overdetermination and the range of an analysis.) In well over-determined cases, back-calculation can give the analyst several useful pieces of information, including a quantitative indication of the quality of the calibration matrix, by determining the average error—the average difference between the known and back-calculated concentrations.

In some cases one component may be determined less accurately than the others. This can indicate that the portion(s) of the spectrum used to determine that component is not appropriate; it may for instance be subject to perturbations. It is also possible to detect gradual deviations from Beer's law at higher concentrations, and it can be easy to flag any sample where the input concentrations were in error. This procedure also provides a rapid method for comparing different choices of bands, baselines, etc. used in the analysis, and is therefore a valuable tool in methods development.

Overdetermination in **K**-Matrix

Just as it is possible to overdetermine the simple one component analysis, so the multicomponent case can be overdetermined. There are two distinct, and nonexclusive types of overdetermination:

(1) *Overdetermination of Data Points*—If there are n-components, then at least n-absorbance values (data points) must be taken from each spectrum. These points must come from regions where the components have significant absorbances. Addition of more useful spectroscopic data from independent samples will tend to reduce the effect of noise in the spectra, and therefore reduce random errors.

(2) *Overdetermination of Calibration Samples*—If there are n-components, then at least n-calibration samples must be run. Calibrating with more samples is similar to use of many samples in the single component case, and better characterizes the calibration matrix. (This is discussed in more detail later.) These overdeterminations can be performed simultaneously, that is, both more data points than necessary, and more standards than required may be employed.

For a system overdetermined in terms of both calibration samples and data points, the matrices may be expressed as

$$
\begin{bmatrix}
A_{11} & A_{12} & \ldots & A_{1m} \\
A_{21} & A_{22} & \ldots & A_{2m} \\
\vdots & \vdots & & \\
A_{j1} & A_{j2} & \ldots & A_{jm}
\end{bmatrix}
=
\begin{bmatrix}
k_{11} & k_{12} & \ldots & k_{1n} \\
k_{21} & k_{22} & \ldots & k_{2n} \\
\vdots & \vdots & & \\
k_{j1} & k_{j2} & \ldots & k_{jn}
\end{bmatrix}
*
\begin{bmatrix}
c_{11} & c_{12} & \ldots & c_{1m} \\
c_{21} & c_{22} & \ldots & c_{2m} \\
\vdots & & & \\
c_{n1} & c_{n2} & \ldots & c_{nm}
\end{bmatrix}
\tag{11}
$$

When $m > n$ the number of mixtures is overdetermined.
When $j > n$ the number of data points is overdetermined.

In overdetermined cases therefore, the **C** and **K** matrices are not square. The mathematics described previously (matrix inversions) perform operations mathematically equivalent to least squares regression in this multidimensional case.

*Intercepts in **K**-Matrix*

The simple formulation of Beer's law given previously, and the methods used for its solution, have the effect of forcing the "calibration curve" to pass through the origin. For a variety of reasons (including the use of local baselines, and curvature in the concentration versus absorbance plot), the best fit may not be a line that passes through the origin. It is mathematically possible to allow an intercept by adding a row of "ones" to the concentration matrix [6]

$$
\begin{bmatrix} A_{11} A_{12} \ldots A_{1m} \\ A_{21} A_{22} \ldots A_{2m} \\ \vdots \quad \vdots \\ A_{j1} A_{12} \ldots A_{jm} \end{bmatrix} = \begin{bmatrix} k_{11} k_{12} \ldots k_{1n} k_{10} \\ k_{21} k_{22} \ldots k_{2n} k_{20} \\ \vdots \quad \vdots \\ k_{j1} k_{j2} \ldots k_{jn} k_{j0} \end{bmatrix} * \begin{bmatrix} c_{11} c_{12} \ldots c_{1m} \\ c_{21} c_{22} \ldots c_{2m} \\ \vdots \\ c_{n1} c_{n2} \ldots c_{nm} \\ 1 \quad 1 \ldots 1 \end{bmatrix} \quad (12)
$$

These ones can be regarded as the concentration of a "dummy" component, and one extra absorbance data point will have to be taken from each spectrum, and one extra standard run.

*Limitations to the **K**-Matrix Approach*

There are some major limitations to the **K**-matrix approach. The matrix of concentration information, **C**, must be inverted during the operations, and it (or more strictly **CC'**) must therefore be nonsingular so that its determinant is nonzero [5]. A matrix becomes singular if there is a linear relation between its component rows or columns. If one row or column of a matrix can be expressed as the weighted sum of the other rows or columns in the matrix, the determinant will be zero, the matrix singular, and hence noninvertable.

Now, it is quite common to analyze for all the components in a chemical system. As Brown, Lynch, Obremski, and Lavery point up [6], if these concentrations are expressed as mole fractions or percentages, the sum of the concentrations of the components in the calibration set will be the same in all the mixtures. If an attempt is made to utilize an intercept, by adding a row of ones, the matrix will become singular, because one row is a constant, and the other rows always sum to a constant. Thus it is not always possible to use an intercept in the **K**-matrix approach.

Similarly, when there are $n - 1$ components of interest in an n-component system, and again concentrations are given as mole fractions or percentages, there is no difference between calibrating using $n - 1$ components with an intercept, and using all n-components. Since the concentration of the last component can be obtained by subtracting the sum of the concentrations of the $n - 1$ components from a constant, the same results will be obtained in each case.

An analyst can unwittingly generate this type of effect by making up standards in which the sum of the concentrations of standards, although not adding to 100%, add to a constant. Consider a case where dilute solutions of A, B, and C in a solvent with noninterfering absorbances are being studied (Table 1). Since Set II has been made up with the sum of the concentrations of A, B, and C equalling a constant, it will exhibit the effect whereas Set I will not.

In a **K**-matrix analysis the concentrations of A, B, and C in the standards must be known. If these concentrations add to a constant as in Set II, it is impossible either to add the concentration of the solvent to the analysis or to make use of an intercept, because a singular matrix will be obtained. However, if Set I of standards is employed it is possible to include either the solvent concentration or an intercept (but not both!) in the analysis. This can be an advantage, as there may be interactions between A, B, C, and the solvent which can be taken into account if the solvent is an explicit part of the analysis. Wherever possible, it is best to avoid the type of constraint generated by the standards of Set II.

A further pitfall from calibration sets like Set II can be seen if the concentrations of the three components are plotted in 3 dimensions. Since the concentrations satisfy the equation $A + B + C$ = constant, they will plot as a plane in the 3 dimensional space with the x-axis being the concentration of A, y the concentration of B, and z, C. It is evident that many real samples from this system will *not* satisfy the constraint $A + B + C$ = constant, and will lie off this plane. Analysis of such samples using this calibration will involve an extrapolation perpendicular to the $A + B + C$ = constant plane rather than an interpolation, and will risk complete failure. A better calibration like Set I scatters its points over the whole volume, so that typical samples fall within the calibration region and are estimated by interpolation.

TABLE 1—*Suitable (Set I) and unsuitable (Set II) calibration standards.*

| | | | Concen | trations | | | |
| | Set | I | | | Set | II | |
A	B	C	Solvent	A	B	C	Solvent
1	2	3	94	1	2	3	94
2	2	1	95	2	3	1	94
3	1	3	93	3	2	1	94
1	3	1	95	1	3	2	94
1	1	2	96	2	1	3	94
3	2	2	93	3	1	2	94

Another failure mode of the **K**-matrix approach occurs when a calibration is made with carefully prepared standards, but the real samples to be analyzed contain impurities that have absorption features in the regions used for the analysis. If, for example, the only absorbance at 2300 cm^{-1} in any of the calibration samples can from component Z, any absorbance in an unknown sample at 2300 cm^{-1} will also be attributed to component Z, and extra absorbance at 2300 cm^{-1} due to an impurity will show up as an enhanced concentration of Z. Therefore, the analysis report would be grossly in error. (If the extra component absorbs in a region used as a local baseline, then it is even possible to obtain an analysis report with "negative" concentrations, because the absorbances can be negative relative to the resulting baseline. In such a case it is more obvious that the analysis has failed.)

Similarly, if an interloper appears in one or more of the calibration samples and overlaps a band being used in the analysis, it will have much the same effect as noise and will result in a substantially poorer calibration, and later, erroneous analyses. Unless the interloper is included in the calibration and its concentration is provided as input to the **K**-matrix calculation (difficult to do for an impurity), its absorbances, in effect, will vary randomly from calibration sample to calibration sample and will decrease the correlation between absorbances and concentrations found by the **K**-matrix calculation.

Therefore, in a **K**-matrix analysis, all potential components must be included in the calibration. This leads to very complex analyses, because as the number of components expands, it is likely that the amount of data required from each spectrum (the number of absorbance values) will expand, and the number of calibration samples must then also be greater. The **P**-matrix approach provides a solution to this problem by another, simpler means.

The **P**-Matrix Approach

The **P**-matrix approach has been described recently by Brown [6–8], who refers to earlier papers in this field [15,16], which presented less complete descriptions of the theory. The key step is changing the formulation of Beer's law to

$$\mathbf{C} = \mathbf{PA} \qquad (13)$$

where

$\mathbf{C}$ = the matrix of concentrations,
$\mathbf{P}$ = the matrix relating absorbance to concentration, and
$\mathbf{A}$ = the matrix of absorbances.

Experimentally, the same procedure is used—first a set of standards is run with components having known concentrations. From the absorbance data the **P**-matrix is calculated

$$P = CA'(AA')^{-1} \tag{14}$$

Then, when an unknown is run, the concentrations can be found immediately

$$C = PA \tag{15}$$

and a second matrix inversion is avoided. The **P**-matrix approach is thus simpler in a mathematical sense, although it is conceptually rather more difficult, because concentrations are given as a function of absorbance, rather than absorbance as a function of concentration, as in the more conventional **K**-matrix formulation.

*Advantages of the **P**-Matrix Approach*

Intercepts are easier to implement in this approach, as it involves adding a row of ones to the absorbances matrix, and it is, therefore, more difficult to get into the situation where an intercept introduces dependencies [7]. The major advantage of this approach, though, is that it is possible to accommodate situations in which impurities are present. Specifically, if there is an impurity present in the calibration samples with varying concentration, the analysis is still possible, even if its concentrations are unknown. It does not have to be included as a known component in order for this to occur. If other analytical frequencies are not affected and influenced by these components, the **P**-matrix will determine correlations between absorbances and concentrations using those frequencies, and those frequencies where the impurity absorbs, in effect, will be ignored.

The mechanics of this can be illustrated by considering a 3-component case, and then the same system, but treated as a 2-component case with a varying impurity. If 5 analytical frequencies are used the matrices will have the following appearance

$$
\begin{bmatrix} C_A \\ C_B \\ C_C \end{bmatrix} =
\begin{bmatrix}
P_{11} & P_{12} & P_{13} & P_{14} & P_{15} \\
P_{21} & P_{22} & P_{23} & P_{24} & P_{25} \\
P_{31} & P_{32} & P_{33} & P_{34} & P_{35}
\end{bmatrix} *
\begin{bmatrix} A_1 \\ A_2 \\ A_3 \\ A_4 \\ A_5 \end{bmatrix} \tag{16}
$$

Thus the concentration of component A is obtained by the matrix multiplication of the first row of the **P**-matrix by the selected absorbance values. If component C is not included in the calibration, the same **P**-matrix is obtained, except that the third row is absent. The coefficients along the first row are exactly the same, because the rows of the **P**-matrix do not interact with one another.

Put in another way, the **P**-matrix method seeks a correlation between concentrations and absorbances. If the impurity absorbs at a particular frequency, then there will be poor correlation between the absorbance at that frequency and the concentration of any of the components for which the calibration was done. Thus, the values of the corresponding coefficients in the **P**-matrix will be close to zero. There is enough data (greater than n-calibration spectra for n-absorbance values) to determine these correlations. This is not the case in a **K**-matrix analysis.

In order for impurities to be discriminated against, samples containing the impurity at various concentration levels, must be included in the calibration set, though the impurity concentrations themselves need not be known. The **P**-matrix method will fail, just like the **K**-matrix method, if "unknown" impurities, not present in the calibration set, appear in the analytical samples, absorbing at frequencies or baseline regions selected for the calibration.

The ability of the **P**-matrix method to work in this way has additional implications that have not been fully explored. For instance, there is the promise that baseline correction (measuring absorbances relative to local baselines) is not required in the data set, if instead the absorbances at one or more baseline frequencies themselves are included in the calibration data. Any baseline offsets or slopes should then be regarded by the **P**-matrix as arising from an additional (nonquantitated) "baseline" component, and therefore be compensated for.

*Limitations to the **P**-Matrix Approach*

The major disadvantage of the **P**-matrix approach concerns the number of calibration samples required. In the **K**-matrix method, if there are n-components, then at least n-calibration samples are needed, and at least n-data points must be abstracted from the spectra. It is quite common to have only a 3 or 4 component mixture, but to utilize the advantages of overdetermination and use 10 to 15 data points, especially if the bands of interest are severely overlapped.

In the **P**-matrix case, if n-components are to be determined, at least n absorbance values (data points) must be used. However, the number of calibration samples must be larger than the number of data points. Thus, in a **K**-matrix case one could have 4 components, 8 calibration samples and yet take 20 data points, but in the **P**-matrix case, if only 8 calibration samples are available, then only 8 data points *can* be employed (and that many only by giving up overdetermination). Conversely, in **P**-matrix, if 20 data points are *required* (for example, for a severely overlapped case), then 20 calibration standards *must* be used. Sample and data overdetermination, therefore, involves more work (making up and running calibration samples), and there exists the dangerous temptation to overdetermine not at all, or only slightly.

Calibration Issues

Importance of Overdetermination

In order to see the significance of overdetermination in valid calibrations, it is useful to distinguish between two components of the analyses' error, which we shall call here *intrinsic error* and *selection effects*. To simplify this discussion, we are ignoring errors arising from an inappropriate choice of the form of the analysis, for example, no intercept where an intercept is required, or a nonlinear interaction between components. Intrinsic error manifests itself in differences between spectra of two samples that are allegedly identical. It comes from two aliquots being slightly different, sample preparation errors, temperature variations between samples, spectrometer noise, etc. Selection effects, on the other hand, are due entirely to the selection of a small number of imperfect spectra on which to base the calibration. If the calibration spectra had no intrinsic error there would be no selection effects, and a "perfect" calibration would ensue, but in practice, an estimated calibration is obtained.

These two sources of error cannot be separated or measured directly in a real case. What can be measured in the *apparent calibration error,* which is determined by applying the calibration matrix to the spectra used in that calculation, and comparing the known (input) concentrations to the calculated concentrations. This comparison can be summarized by a single number which is the average of the absolute values of the difference between the known and calculated concentrations.

The *experimental analysis* error is the difference between the calculated and known concentration in an analytical sample, not one of the calibration samples. This includes the intrinsic error of the analytical sample, in addition to the errors in the calibration. If we could analyze a "perfect" spectrum (one with no intrinsic error), we would obtain the difference between the known and calculated concentration which would be a measure of the actual error of the calibration process. We shall call this the *actual calibration error.* The results of analyzing other samples may give greater or lesser errors, but the dependency of the errors on the number of calibration samples will be the same.

Selection effects can act to make the apparent calibration error small, and in the exactly determined case (number of components equals the number of calibration spectra in a **K**-matrix analysis), selection effects produce an apparent calibration error of zero. If overdetermination is modest (for example, only one or two extra samples), the apparent calibration error can be found to be slight. This is an extension of behavior in the familiar 1-component case where the correlation coefficient for a data set can actually decline as data are added, while one's confidence that a reliable and rugged calibration is obtained actually increases.

To illustrate these considerations, a set of 20 synthetic, noiseless, 4-component mixture spectra were constructed. To each was added an equal amount of noise. The noise spectrum was typical of that encountered in normal spectra, different for each sample, and scaled to be very large (about 2% of typical peak heights) to emphasize its effect. A series of calibrations was performed using 4 to 18 samples, and these were used to analyse a noise-free spectrum which was not in the calibration set. Thus we can obtain the apparent and actual calibration errors as a function of the number of calibration samples, and these data are presented in Fig. 1.

There are several salient features. To begin with, the plots both blow up for the exactly determined case of only four calibration samples. As expected, the apparent calibration error is zero, while the actual calibration error is very large, because the calibration has been distorted to exactly fit both the spectra and the noise of the four calibration samples. Had a dif-

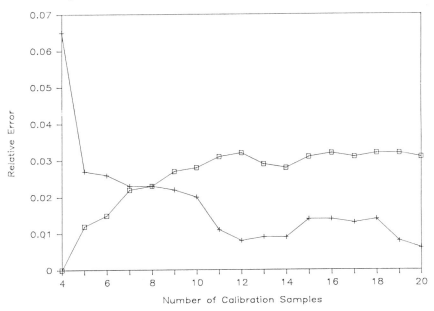

□ apparent error.
+ Actual error.

FIG. 1—*Actual and apparent error as a function of overdetermination.*

ferent set of four been chosen, a different (perhaps wildly different) calibration would have ensued.

As further calibration spectra are added, the analysis error drops towards zero. This is expected as the additional spectra cause the effects of noise to average out. Note that only one additional calibration spectrum is needed to eliminate the worst effects of fitting the idiosyncracies of the individual samples. If the noise in the spectra were the only complication, as it is in this case, then the actual calibration error would tend to zero as the number of calibration samples tends to infinity.

Overdetermination can be looked at as a form of signal averaging which decreases the effect of irrelevant spectral features (noise, artifacts, sampling problems, etc.) compared to the underlying signal. Increasing the number of calibration spectra gives the analysis more data to work with, and, thus, a better ability to discriminate between signal and noise.

However, as spectra are added, the apparent calibration error rises. Where the number of calibration spectra is small, the selection effect compensates in part for the intrinsic error. As the number of samples approaches infinity, the apparent error will tend towards a constant that is a function of the added noise only. With an infinite number of calibration samples, the noise will be averaged out, a perfect analysis is obtained, and the difference between the known and calculated results for each spectrum merely reflects the noise in that particular spectrum.

The key question here is how can the analyst tell if adequate overdetermination has been done in the real case? One approach is to first calibrate using $(n - 1)$ samples where n are available. The apparent calibration error is then compared to the analysis error for the nth sample. This procedure may be repeated with a different spectrum selected for analysis each time. If the calibration error is substantially smaller than the analysis error, then it is likely that selection effects are producing an unreliable calibration, and that extra calibration samples are required. The apparent calibration error may increase on addition of calibration samples, as shown in Fig. 1, but a better calibration should be obtained.

This is very well illustrated in Table 2, where, due to a limited number of calibrated samples, only three mixtures were available to calibrate a 2-component system. The average percentage errors for the unknown samples (the two samples not used in the calibration) are 4 to 5 times larger than the average percentage errors for the calibration samples. (This analysis is discussed further in the section entitled "A Highly Overlapped Case.") The apparently better calibration is due to a fitting of the noise and other random data in the spectra, the selection effect. The presence of a selection effect, as evidenced by the apparent calibration error being much smaller than the actual calibration, is a strong indication that a greater degree of overdetermination will improve the quality of the analysis.

In every case, including that where only a small number of samples is available, it is profitable to run each sample twice and use both spectra in

TABLE 2—*Analytical results for two organic salts in aqueous solution.*

Sample	Component A		Component B	
	Known	Measured	Known	Measured
	CALIBRATION STANDARDS			
1	65.0	64.96	35.0	35.04
2	60.0	60.03	40.0	39.97
3	55.0	55.02	45.0	44.98
Average % errors		0.05%		0.08%
	ANALYTICAL RESULTS			
4	62.5	62.30	37.5	37.70
5	57.5	57.59	42.5	42.41
Average % errors		0.24%		0.37%

the calibration step. This will reduce the effects of intrinsic error, give a good indication as to the magnitude of that intrinsic error, and, if samples are run in a random order, can highlight possible carry-over effects. These can happen, for instance, if a liquid cell is inadequately cleaned between samples.

Appropriate Calibration Samples

Apart from the degree of overdetermination, there are other factors that influence the quality of a calibration. First, the accuracy of a calibration is dependent upon the accuracy of the standards used. If there is a systematic error in the concentrations of the standards used, then a systematic error will be present in the concentrations reported for analytes. If there are random errors in the concentrations of the standards, then there will still be errors in the reported concentrations. However, in the latter case, over-determination of calibration samples can reduce these errors, via the least squares fit, as shown previously.

Second, the samples themselves must be independent. In a simple three component case, with 4 calibration samples, Sets III and IV shown in Table 3 will fail, whereas Set V is reasonable. In Set III, the first three samples can be obtained simply by diluting the fourth, and no independent information is available for any of the components. In Set IV, the third and fourth

TABLE 3—*Dependent (Sets III and IV) and independent (Set V) calibration samples.*

Set III			Set IV			Set V		
				COMPONENT				
A	B	C	A	B	C	A	B	C
				CONCENTRATIONS				
1	1	1	1	1	1	1	1	1
2	2	2	3	2	1	3	2	1
3	3	3	4	3	2	2	3	4
4	4	4	5	4	3	4	5	3

samples can be obtained by appropriately mixing the first two, and again there is insufficient independent information.

Last, the factors mentioned previously (Limitations of the **K**-Matrix Approach), that sample concentrations should not add to a constant, if possible, is also very significant.

Calibration With Mixtures

A key feature of **K**- (and **P**-) matrix analyses is calibration with mixtures. If Beer's law were obeyed precisely, and the various components did not interact with one another, perturbing each other's spectra, then calibration with pure samples would work perfectly. Indeed, there are cases where this is true, for instance, low pressure gases. However, in most cases there are significant interactions between the components, and it is found that the spectrum of pure component *A* can be quite different from that of *A* in the presence of *B*.

Spectral fitting methods [9,10], commonly use the spectra of pure components. This is mathematically equivalent to using a **K**- or **P**-matrix method, and instead of calibrating with mixtures, calibrating using pure samples. More advanced spectral fitting methods, combined with factor analysis for example [11,12], can abstract the spectra of components from mixtures and use these for calibration. This is approximately equivalent to calibrating a **K**- or **P**-matrix method with mixture spectra. Because the **K**- and **P**-matrix methods recognize that spectral perturbations occur, it follows that the calibrations are only valid over certain concentration ranges. Indeed, the critical question is over what range is a calibration valid or useful, and this is examined in detail in the section "Valid Regions of a Multicomponent Analysis."

Examples and Discussion

Analysis for a Minor Component

In order to illustrate some of the points described previously, the comparatively simple example of analyzing for an additive in pressed films of polyethylene is examined. Five standards were available, with the additive concentration varying from 0.4 to 1.2%, and the films were about 500 μm thick; the exact thicknesses were determined using an automatic micrometer. First, the spectra were measured, and a typical spectrum, shown in Fig. 2, demonstrates that the major polyethylene bands are very strong, with many being greater than 3*A*. Second, bands arising from the additive were identified. This could have been done by manual examination of the spectra, but instead an "activity spectrum" (Fig. 3) was calculated. This is a plot of frequency versus the standard deviation of the absorbance in this group of five spectra. In such a plot the polyethylene features, because they are constant in the set of absorbance spectra, will be very small, but the

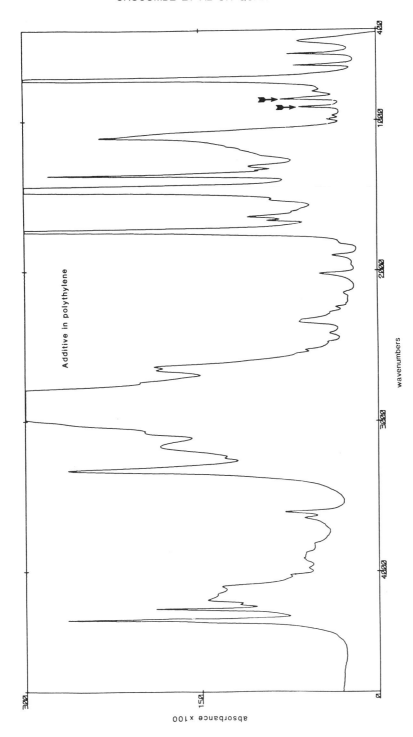

FIG. 2—*FT-IR spectrum of a polyethylene film, about 500 μm thick, containing 1.2% of an additive. The bands marked are an additive band and a polyethylene band, suitable for use as an internal thickness standard.*

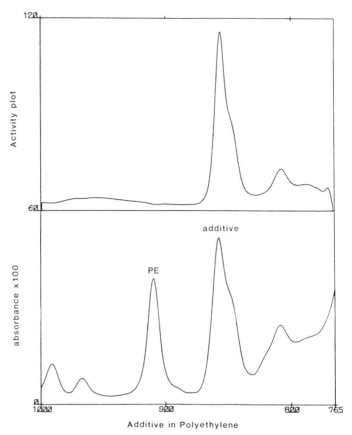

FIG. 3—*FT-IR spectrum (1000 to 765 cm^{-1}) of a polyethylene film containing 1.2% of an additive* (bottom), *and an activity spectrum* (top) *of a set of samples with differing concentrations* (see text).

additive features will be emphasized. Thus, Fig. 3 shows that the band at 863 cm^{-1} is due to the additive, as well as the low frequency shoulder at about 840 cm^{-1}. It can also be seen that the band at 910 cm^{-1} is due to polyethylene, with no contribution from the additive. Of course, if a sample of the pure additive were available, a suitable band could have been selected from that spectrum. However, the activity spectrum method has the advantages of not requiring pure samples, determining the additive spectrum in the presence of the polyethylene, and making it simple to select a band of appropriate intensity.

The 863 cm^{-1} band is about 0.5 A in the most concentrated sample, and is therefore a good band to use for quantitative analysis. Similarly the 910 cm^{-1} band, at about 0.4 A, is a suitable candidate for use as a measure of sample thickness. Frequencies suitable for use as local baselines can also be selected, and are designated by the arrows in Fig. 4.

Even in this simple case there are many mathematical approaches to the analysis. First, to account for variable pathlengths in both calibration and analytical samples, one can use a band ratio method, employing the polyethylene band as a measure of sample thickness, or, alternatively, directly input the measured sample thickness. If this latter course is taken, the thickness of all the samples to be analyzed will have to be recorded, and these values will then be entered in the analysis. This is a clear opportunity for error. Second, the data used in the analysis could be absorbances at the peak maxima, integrated absorbances, or a grid of absorbance values taken over the bands. Last, the analysis could allow an intercept, or alternatively force the calibration curve to pass through the origin.

The results of seven different mathematical approaches are shown in Table 4. In all cases the same spectra were used, and, because of the small number of standards available, the **K**-matrix approach was employed. The

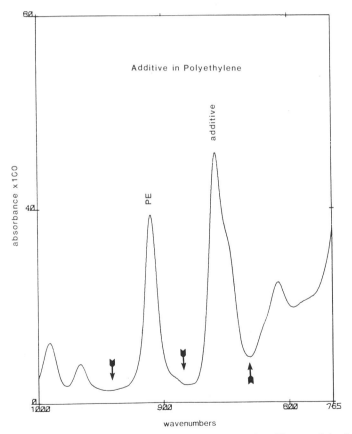

FIG. 4—*FT-IR spectrum (1000 to 765 cm⁻¹) of a polyethylene film containing 1.2% of an additive, indicating analytical bands and basepoints.*

TABLE 4—*Results of seven different mathematical approaches to a minor component analysis.*

Number	Pathlength Method[a]	Intercept	Type[b]	Average Error	Systematic/ Random
1	BR	No	max	0.033	S[c]
2	BR	No	area	0.049	S[c]
3	M	No	max	0.018	R
4	M	No	area	0.006	R
5	M	No	grid	0.018	S[d]
6	BR	Yes	max	0.013	R
7	BR	Yes	area	0.013	S[d]

NOTE—By allowing an intercept the errors reported in 1 and 2 are substantially reduced in 6 and 7. The concentration range of the additive was from 0.2 to 1.2%; see text for details.

[a] BR = band ratio; M = measured.

[b] Max = absorbance at 863 cm^{-1}; Area = integrated area from 870 to 840 cm^{-1}; and Grid = grid of absorbance values from 870 to 840 cm^{-1} at 4 cm^{-1} intervals.

[c] Low for low concentrations, high for high concentrations.

[d] High for low and high concentrations, low for medium concentrations.

average error is the result of back-calculating all the concentrations and taking the average of the absolute values of the differences between the back-calculated values and the known value. Thus, for Case 1 a concentration of 1% might be subject to an error of ±0.033% absolute.

Two points emerge immediately. There is a variation in the average errors of almost an order of magnitude—from a low of 0.006 to a high of 0.049—and some of the errors appear to be systematic, while others are random. The errors themselves are quite small, and in a practical case, may be of limited concern. However, if close monitoring of this additive level were required (for example, for cost or property-modification considerations), they would be significant. It is also worth noting that the differences disclosed here might be completely submerged if either the spectra were noisy, or if the absorbances were measured by hand.

It is important that errors appear to be random if any attempt is made to extrapolate the calibration curve—to use this calibration for concentrations higher or lower than any sample in the calibration set. It is highly likely that errors outside the calibration range will be much larger if calibration errors are systematic than if calibration errors were of the same magnitude but random.

One cause of systematic errors has already been alluded to—the use of local baselines—and the origin of this is shown in Fig. 5. The lower spectrum shows a synthetic case, similar to the polyethylene additive, with two relatively narrow, weak bands lying between strong, broad bands. The upper spectrum shows the overlapped spectrum decomposed into its component bands. The conventional approach is to measure the height of the bands relative to a local baseline, and this is shown for the 1600 cm^{-1} band. The arrows indicate the basepoints chosen. In the upper half of the figure the

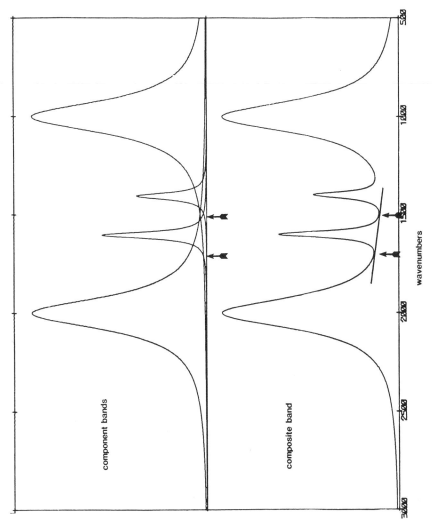

FIG. 5—Synthetic spectra demonstrating the effect of local baselines.

basepoints are again indicated by arrows, and it can be seen that the absorbance at the basepoints themselves includes a contribution for the 1600 cm^{-1} band. Therefore, measuring the absorbance of the narrow bands at 1400 and 1600 cm^{-1} relative to local baselines does not give a true indication of their intensities, and a plot of baseline-relative absorbance versus concentration will not pass through the origin.

From the statistical analysis the apparent best approach is Case 4, using integrated areas and measured pathlengths. Because of the potential problems in measuring pathlengths and entering the data, Case 6, using absorbance maxima and a band ratio method, might be preferred in practice.

Thus, even in a simple case it is profitable to examine a number of different approaches and determine which gives the best statistical results. If another additive band with intensity in the appropriate range had been found, it would have been useful to use that as well; had more samples been available a **P**-matrix approach could have been attempted. Not only is the average error an important factor in deciding upon one method, but whether that error is systematic or random is significant. The immunity of the analysis to pathlength variation is also critical in this case. Last, a factor not explored here is the effect of noise in the spectra. In most cases, especially where FT-IR instruments are employed, noise is not a problem. However, in some special cases (for example, rapid quantitation of microscopic samples, or very low concentration gases) noise will be a factor, and it may be important to select bands in relatively low-noise portions of the spectrum.

A Highly Overlapped Case

Figures 6 and 7 are spectra of two organic salts in aqueous solution, and Fig. 8 shows the spectra of the salts in the region 2000 to 800 cm^{-1}, with the water subtracted. Clearly the spectra of the two salts completely overlap each other, and no features unique to either compound can be identified. Again, in this case only five calibration standards were available. The desired datum was the ratio of the salt concentrations, not their absolute values, and therefore in Table 4 the concentrations are expressed as parts out of a total of 100.

Because of the limited number of standards, three were used for the calibration, and the remaining two were used as a check. These two had concentration ratios within the bounds of the other three. The results are shown in Table 2, and these demonstrate the success of the **K**-matrix method in analyzing these completely overlapped spectra. As discussed earlier, due to the lack of substantial overdetermination, the average percent errors in the calibration spectrum are 4 to 5 times smaller than the average percent errors in the unknowns.

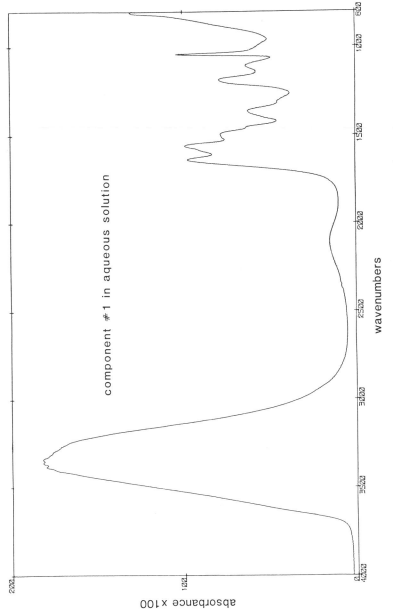

FIG. 6—*FT-IR ATR spectrum of organic salt No. 1 in aqueous solution.*

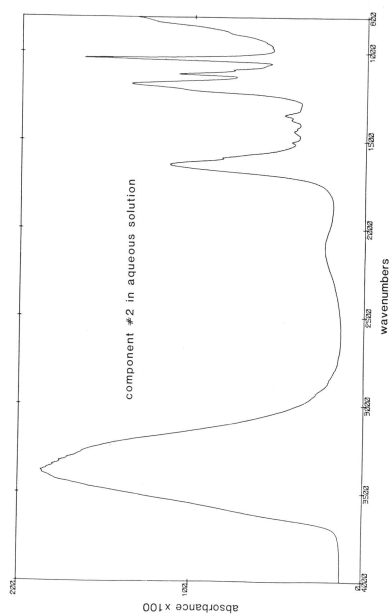

FIG. 7—*FT-IR ATR spectrum of organic salt No. 2 in aqueous solution.*

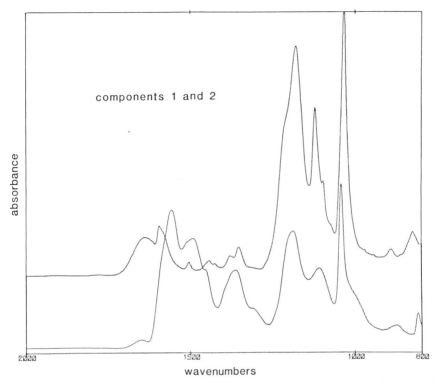

absorbance

components 1 and 2

wavenumbers

2000   1500   1000   800

FIG. 8—*FT-IR ATR spectra of the two organic salts in aqueous solution, after spectral subtraction of water spectrum.*

There is one further interesting point in this analysis. The water subtraction, used in Fig. 8, was done solely for aesthetic reasons, that is, to enable the component spectra to be clearly seen; the spectra used in the analysis were not treated in this way. Such a subtraction is not necessary because the water merely provides a constant background, and local baselines can be used to descriminate against this. More importantly, spectral subtractions frequently involve the subjective judgment of the analyst in selecting the optimum subtraction factor. A constant subtraction factor does not affect the analysis and therefore is irrelevant, while a nonconstant factor will perturb the spectra in a nonreproducible way. Relying on a software routine to do the subtraction can lead to problems if the routine used is sensitive to varying amounts of (for instance) water vapor in the spectra. If aqueous solutions are being examined then absorbances due to water vapor may be present in the spectra, and erroneous subtraction factors could well be generated, and causing the analysis to fail. The use of unmodified aqueous solution spectra has been briefly discussed elsewhere [17].

Valid Region of a Multicomponent Analysis

In simple cases the region for which an analysis is valid can be seen easily. In the polyethylene additive case, having selected a calibration where the errors appeared to be small and random, there is great confidence that it is valid for additive concentrations between 0.4 and 1.2%, and some extrapolation of the calibration curve is possible to concentrations lower than 0.4% and higher than 1.2%. The ability to extrapolate is important, because if a production process is badly adjusted, then it is likely that component concentrations will fall outside the usual region, and knowledge of the actual concentrations, and thus of the degree of maladjustment is important.

In this example, the calibration may be reasonable up to additive concentrations of 2%, but after that several effects come into play and the results obtained are unlikely to be trustworthy. For instance, at an additive concentration of 2%, the band used will have an absorbance approaching 1, and may show deviations from Beer's law. In addition, the concentration of polyethylene in the sample is beginning to fall from close to 100 to 98%, and a band ratio method is no longer strictly valid, since it assumes a polyethylene concentration of 100%. In general, the further a calibration is extrapolated, the greater the potential errors. It is difficult to give a general quantitative measure, but an extrapolation of 10 to 20% may be reasonable, and an extrapolation of 100% (that is, doubling a maximum concentration) is likely to be unreliable.

In multicomponent analyses we acknowledge that compounds perturb one another's spectra; therefore, it is no longer appropriate to view their concentrations in isolation. For instance, if one component is out of the calibration range, then it is possible that the analysis for the remaining components is invalid, even though their concentrations are in range. The spectral perturbations induced by the out-of-range component may cause the whole analysis to be defective.

A standard may be thought of occupying a portion of "calibration space." For instance, in a one component case, if we have standards of concentrations 2, 4, 6, 8, 10, and obtain a well-behaved calibration curve, we assume that a concentration of 5 is "covered" by samples of concentrations 4 and 6. Such a curve is simple, with the absorbance axis and a single concentration axis. A sample may be thought of as making the calibration valid for a certain distance along the concentration axis on either side of its position. In an n-component case we still have a single absorbance axis, but now we have n-orthogonal concentration axes, and a sample renders a concentration valid for a certain hypervolume of n-dimensional concentration space around a point. This can be difficult to visualize, but can be illustrated by a 2-component example (Fig. 9). The data points in this figure represent calibration samples, and the calibration is reliable within the enclosed area only, where a result is generated by an interpolation process, rather than extrapolation. The generation of appropriate samples is sometimes termed "designing the box," for reasons that are clear in Fig. 9.

As the number of components increases, the situation becomes more complex. Table 5 gives hypothetical data for an overdetermined 3-component case, calibrated using 6 standards, whose concentrations are stated. The "analytical samples," also noted in this table, have concentrations of their individual components that fall within the range of the concentrations of the individual components in the standards, between 1 and 10, but they are *not* strictly within the calibration range. For instance, there is no calibration sample in which the concentrations of all three components are high, as in analyte I; there are no samples in which even two of the concentrations are as high as in analyte II, and there is no calibration sample similar to analyte III. In order for the calibration to be valid for these analyte samples, extra standards, of the type designated 7 to 12, should be included in the calibration set. It is clear that in order to cover all cases where A, B, and C can independently have concentrations between 1 and 10, even more

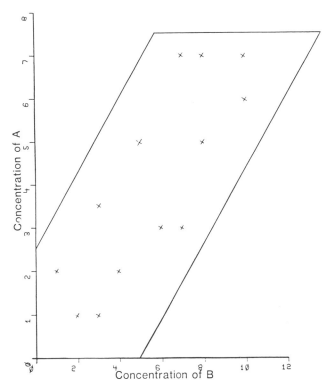

FIG. 9—*The data points represent calibration samples, and the valid region of the analysis is enclosed. Samples whose concentrations lie outside the enclosed region may not be analyzed correctly.*

TABLE 5—*Calibration standards and the valid range of a multicomponent analysis.*

Sample Number	Concentrations		
	A	B	C
CALIBRATION SAMPLES			
1	1	5	10
2	5	10	1
3	10	1	5
4	1	1	5
5	1	5	1
6	5	1	1
ANALYTE SAMPLES			
I	8	8	8
II	1	10	10
III	5	5	10
EXTRA CALIBRATION SAMPLES			
7	10	10	10
8	11	9	7
9	4	6	9
10	7	4	11
11	1	9	11
12	2	12	8

NOTE—Analyte Samples I, II, and III do not strictly lie in the range of the analysis generated by Calibration Samples 1 to 6; in order to analyse them accurately the extra Calibration Samples 7 to 12 should be included.

calibration samples, even as many as 20 in all, need to be included. If these components do indeed perturb each other's spectra significantly, then it may be advisable to develop several separate analyses (several "boxes") to encompass the full range.

Extensions to Other Sampling Techniques

The mathematical methods described previously assume Beer's law, a linear relationship between absorbance and concentration. However, these methods can be extended to any case where a similar linear relationship is found or postulated. Spectral intensity may be measured in units other than absorbance when different sampling techniques are used, and if a property of a material can be linearly correlated with spectral features, then that property, rather than concentration, can be measured. If the relationship between "spectral intensity" and concentration is nonlinear, it may be modelled by linear calibration curves over small concentration ranges. In this way it is possible to extend **K**- and **P**-matrix methods to samples studied by techniques like diffuse reflectance and photoacoustic spectroscopy. (Linear fits of nonlinear data, for example, absorbance or concentration squared, could also be used. However, it is noteworthy that extrapolation of such fits will tend to be much less reliable than those using linear data, as the effect of quadratic functions, intended as small correction terms only, can increase very rapidly.)

Diffuse Reflectance

An example of the application of diffuse reflectance [18] is the quantitation of a low level organic additive on a mineral. Figure 10 shows spectra of both the base material and the base material plus additive. These were obtained by diffuse reflectance, using undiluted samples, and are plotted with the vertical axis in Kubelka-Munk units. If these two spectra are subtracted (Fig. 11), then the contribution of the organic additive can be seen more clearly. The spectra used were of neat samples, rather than samples diluted in potassium bromide (KBr), because the spectrum of the additive was of prime interest, not that of the bulk material. A simple approach to the analysis was used, with a grid of 15 data points taken over the additive band using a **K**-matrix approach. Three calibrated samples were available; the concentration of the additive in the most concentrated sample was roughly double that of the least concentrated sample. The analysis reproduced their concentrations with an average relative error of less than 1%. This result demonstrates that diffuse reflectance can be used for this type of quantitative analysis with the required accuracy, especially if the concentration range to be spanned is modest.

Photoacoustic Spectroscopy

In the plastics industry many polymer mixtures are manufactured in pellet form, and there is great interest in rapidly determining their composition with an accuracy of about ±1% [19,20]. Current analyses of pellets involve preparation of hot pressed films, solutions or cast films [21–23], and can be very time consuming. If sample preparation could be minimized, the procedure would be faster, and the possibility then exists of better control of a manufacturing process, resulting in better quality maintenance of the product and less reject material. FT-IR photoacoustic spectroscopy offers the prospect of minimal sample preparation time and is, therefore, very attractive for a quality control environment.

FT-IR photoacoustic spectroscopy has been extensively reviewed [24,25], and, therefore, will not be described in detail here. One of the first applications investigated was the quantitative accuracy, both from the point of view of spectral subtraction and also that of actual quantitation [26–30]. Polymer species investigated include butadiene-acrylonitrile[29], phenolic resins [29] and vinyl chloride-vinyl acetate [30]. The last copolymer has also been investigated by near-IR PAS [31]. Other quantitative work has involved catalyst surfaces [32].

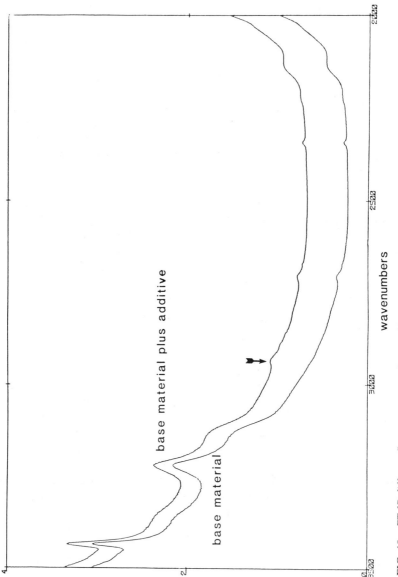

FIG. 10—*FT-IR diffuse reflectance spectra of mineral* (lower spectrum) *and mineral plus organic additive* (upper spectrum).

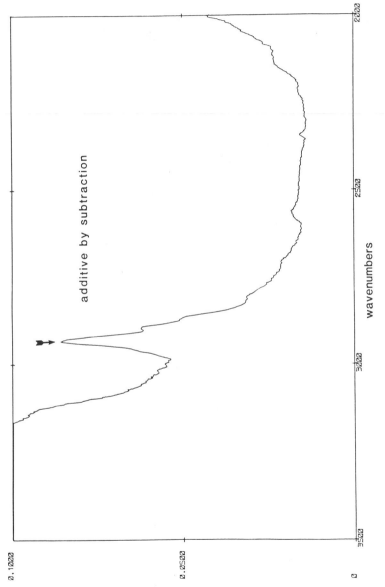

FIG. 11—*FT-IR diffuse reflectance spectrum of additive, obtained by spectral subtraction.*

The approach taken in this work involves recording the photoacoustic spectra of polymer pellets, without any sample preparation, and ratioing the spectra against that of carbon black. These ratioed spectra are then employed in **K**- and **P**-matrix analyses; no further mathematical manipulations or corrections were applied. It is a common perception that FT-IR photoacoustic spectra have low signal to noise, but a spectrum of polystyrene beads, recorded with only 240 s acquisition time, is shown in Fig. 12. Clearly, it is possible to record spectra of polymer pellets with signal-to-noise of 500:1 or better with data collection times of 4 min or less. However, if the signal-to-noise ratio in the photoacoustic spectrum is indeed low (for example, only 100:1), then this will limit the accuracy attainable in an analysis.

In practical examples, we have found that complex mixtures (3 or 4 major components, 1 or 2 minor components) can be analyzed in pellet form successfully. The accuracy for major components (those having concentrations in the 10 to 70% range) is about ±1% (absolute) in cases where the spectra are largely overlapped, and about ±0.5% where discrete bands can

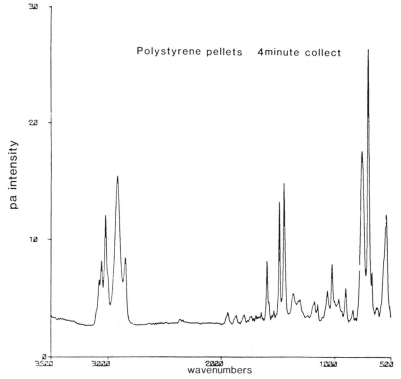

FIG. 12—*FT-IR photoacoustic spectrum of polystyrene pellets. A 4 min acquisition time was used.*

be found. For additives in simple polymers, quantitation at the 1% additive level is possible, with an error of ±0.2%.

The theory of quantitative FT-IR photoacoustic spectroscopy is still in its infancy [24,25], but these results demonstrate that under carefully controlled conditions, with samples having essentially similar surfaces, there is found an empirical linear relationship between concentration and PAS intensity over limited concentration ranges.

Microsampling

There has been a recent explosion of interest in FT-IR microscopy, and in certain cases this technique may be used quantitatively. These are situations where a small area of a large, approximately homogeneous, sample is examined. Examples are the study of trends in the concentrations of additives across polymer films or silicon wafers. In these cases there is good control of sample thickness (or band ratio methods are effective) and diffraction effects are not significant. However, quantitative analysis of physically small samples (for example, 50 μm or less) is inherently difficult. For instance, when small diameter (for example, 5 to 10 μm) single fibers or hairs are examined, the infrared radiation can diffract around the sample, leading to "stray light" problems and absorbance linearity distortions. Hairs and fibers also tend to have circular cross sections, and therefore pathlengths are nonuniform across the sample, as well as being too thick for good quantitative work. In such cases it is possible to obtain spectra better suited to quantitative study by first flattening the sample to a uniform thickness, suitable for IR transmission, in a diamond anvil cell [33]; however, this is done at the expense of destroying the original physical form of the sample.

Caveats and Conclusions

Reproducible Sample Handling

In every type of quantitative analysis care must be taken to ensure that sample form and preparation is reproducible, and that the sample is presented to the spectrometer in a way that allows accurate quantitation. For instance, in transmission spectroscopy the sample should have a uniform thickness and be homogeneous. If these requirements are not met, then serious distortions in relative band intensities arise [34]. In diffuse reflectance the sample cup must be filled to the same level, packed to the same degree, and precautions taken to minimize the specular component. In addition, the samples should have the same particle size distribution. These precautions were all observed in the diffuse reflectance sample described previously. In photoacoustic analyses, the sample cup must be filled to the same level in all cases, and samples left in the accessory for an identical short time before the accessory is sealed and spectra acquired, to allow for temperature equilibration. Band ratio methods can be used to compensate for small differences in the overall signal intensity observed.

In many cases it is valuable to leave a sample in an accessory and monitor the spectrum as a function of time. For instance, it is well known [35] that protein is rapidly adsorbed onto an ATR crystal from flowing blood; therefore, any quantitative analysis of a biological fluid using ATR should be approached with caution.

Thus, as the quantitative possibilities of new sampling techniques are probed, special care must be taken. No sampling method or new algorithm can compensate for gross sampling variation. Finally, an analytical chemist should always be aware of the standard "extra" bands that can be found in infrared spectra [36]. When unfamiliar technology is first employed there are new extra bands to be found, and a recent addition to the canon is a broad feature centered at about 3300 cm^{-1}. This may be due to ice buildup inside an MCT detector whose dewar requires re-evacuation.

Future Developments

We have outlined the theory of **K**- and **P**-matrix multicomponent analysis, and indicated the precautions that should be taken if one is to obtain reliable results, and presented some examples. The scope of such analyses is growing rapidly, aided by the developments in computer-based infrared spectroscopy. As the power of infrared data systems grows, we can expect to see many advances in multicomponent analysis, as well as the routine extension to aqueous solutions, diffuse reflectance, photoacoustic spectroscopy, and microscopic samples, as outlined previously. We can also expect further development of the mathematical methods, including detailed examination of the use of derivative and deconvoluted spectra, reconstruction of experimental spectra, more advanced treatment of errors, determination of properties as well as concentrations, and the promise of software that automatically determines the optimum spectral regions and guides the operator in selection of calibration samples. However, we must be cautious about completely automated systems; they can be completely impossible to deal with if something goes wrong!

Experimental

Spectra were obtained using Digilab (Cambridge, Massachusetts) FTS 90 and Qualimatic FT-IR spectrometers. For spectra obtained on the FTS 90, quantitative determinations were performed using Digilab Quantate and Quantpak software, running on a Data General Nova 4 minicomputer with 128 kbytes memory. Synthetic spectra and noise spectra were generated using FORTRAN programs. For spectra obtained on the Qualimatic, quantitative determinations were performed using Digilab Mult1 and Mult2 software, running on the Qualimatic's Motorola 68000 microprocessor system with 384 kbytes memory.

Sampling accessories employed were Barnes Spectra-Tech (Stamford, Connecticut) diffuse reflectance and cylindrical ATR accessories, and a Digilab photoacoustic accessory.

References

[1] Perry, J. A., *Applied Spectroscopy Review*, Vol. 3, 1970, p. 229.
[2] Conley, R. T., *Infrared Spectroscopy*, Allyn and Bacon, Boston, 1972, Chapter 8.
[3] Potts, W. J., *Chemical Infrared Spectroscopy, Volume 1, Techniques*, Wiley, New York, 1963, Chapter 6.
[4] Smith, A. L., *Applied Infrared Spectroscopy: Fundamentals, Techniques and Applied Problem Solving*, Wiley, New York, 1979, Chapter 6.
[5] Bauman, R. P., *Absorption Spectroscopy*, Wiley, New York, 1962, Chapter 9.
[6] Brown, C. W., Lynch, P. F., Obremski, R. J., and Lavery, D. S., *Analytical Chemistry*, Vol. 54, 1982, p. 1472.
[7] Maris, M. A., Brown, C. W., and Lavery, D. S., *Analytical Chemistry*, Vol. 55, 1983, p. 1694.
[8] Brown, C. W., *Journal of Testing and Evaluation*, Vol. 12, 1984, p. 86.
[9] Antoon, M. K., Koenig, J. H., and Koenig, J. L., *Applied Spectroscopy*, Vol. 31, 1977, p. 518.
[10] Haaland, D. M. and Easterling, R. G., *Applied Spectroscopy*, Vol. 36, 1982, p. 665.
[11] Gillette, P. C., Lando, J. L., and Koenig, J. L., *Analytical Chemistry*, Vol. 55, 1983, p. 630.
[12] Culler, S. R., Gillette, P. C., Ishida, H., and Koenig, J. L., *Applied Spectroscopy*, Vol. 38, 1984, p. 495.
[13] Hanna, A., Marshall, J. C., and Isenhour, T. L., *Journal of Chromatographic Science*, Vol. 17, 1979, p. 434.
[14] Lowry, S. R. and Huppler, D. A., *Analytical Chemistry*, Vol. 53, 1981, p. 889.
[15] Sternberg, J. C., Stillo, H. S., and Schendemann, R. H., *Analytical Chemistry*, Vol. 32, 1960, p. 84.
[16] Barnett, H. A. and Bartoli, A., *Analytical Chemistry*, Vol. 32, 1960, p. 1153.
[17] Kuehl, D. and Crocombe, R. A., *Applied Spectroscopy*, Vol. 38, 1984, p. 907.
[18] Griffiths, P. R. and Fuller, M. P., "Mid-Infrared Spectrometry of Powdered Samples" in *Advances in Infrared and Raman Spectroscopy*, R. E. Hester and R. J. H. Clark, Eds., Heyden, London, 1981, Chapter 2.
[19] Wehrenberg, R. H., *Modern Engineering*, August 1982, pp. 36–42.
[20] Wehrenberg, R. H., *Modern Engineering*, February 1983, pp. 26–30.
[21] Hampton, R. R., *Rubber Chemistry and Technology*, Vol. 45, 1972, p. 546.
[22] Zichy, V. J. I., "Quantitative Infrared Analysis of Polymeric Materials" in *Laboratory Methods in Infrared Spectroscopy*, R. J. G. Miller and B. C. Stace, Eds., Heyden, New York, 1972, Chapter 5.
[23] Haslam, J., Willis, H. A., and Squirrell, D. C. M., *Identification and Analysis of Plastics*, Heyden, New York, pp. 18–34.
[24] McClelland, J. F., *Analytical Chemistry*, Vol. 55, 1983, p. 89A.
[25] Vidrine, D. W., "Photoacoustic Fourier Transform Infrared Spectroscopy of Solids and Liquids," in *Fourier Transform Infrared Spectroscopy*, J. R. Ferraro and L. J. Basile, Eds., Academic Press, New York, 1982, Volume 3, Chapter 4.
[26] Rockley, M. G., Davis, D. M., and Richardson, H. H., *Applied Spectroscopy*, Vol. 35, 1981, p. 185.
[27] Rockley, M. G., Woodard, M., Richardson, H. H., Davis, D. M., Purdie, N., and Bowen, J. M., *Analytical Chemistry*, Vol. 55, 1983, p. 32.
[28] Krishnan, K., *Applied Spectroscopy*, Vol. 35, 1981, p. 549.

[29] Teramae, N., Hiroguchi, M., and Tanaka, S., *Bulletin of the Chemical Society of Japan,* Vol. 55, 1982, p. 2097.

[30] Chalmers, J. M., Stay, B. J., Kirkbright, G. F., Spillane, D. E. M., and Beadle, B. C., *Analyst,* Vol. 106, 1981, p. 1179.

[31] Kirkbright, G. F. and Menon, K. R., *Analytica Chemica Acta,* Vol. 136, 1982, p. 373.

[32] Gardella, J. A., Jr., Jiang, D-A., and Eyring, E. M., *Applied Spectroscopy,* Vol. 37, 1983, p. 131.

[33] Krishnan, K., personal communication.

[34] Davies, B., McNeish, A., Poliakoff, M., and Turner, J. J., *Chemical Physics Letters,* Vol. 52, 1977, p. 477.

[35] Gendreau, R. M., Winters, S., Leininger, R. I., Fink, D., Hassler, C. R., and Jakobsen, R. J., *Applied Spectroscopy,* Vol. 35, 1981, p. 353.

[36] Launer, P. J., "Tracking Down Spurious Bands in Infrared Analysis" in *Laboratory Methods in Infrared Spectroscopy,* R. J. G. Miller and B. C. Stace, Eds., Heyden, New York, 1972, pp. xvii–xxi.

Gregory L. McClure,[1] Patricia B. Roush,[1] J. Fenton Williams,[1] and Craig A. Lehmann[2]

Application of Computerized Quantitative Infrared Spectroscopy to the Determination of the Principal Lipids Found in Blood Serum

REFERENCE: McClure, G. L., Roush, P. B., Williams, J. F., and Lehmann, C. A., "Application of Computerized Quantitative Infrared Spectroscopy to the Determination of the Principal Lipids Found in Blood Serum," *Computerized Quantitative Infrared Analysis, ASTM STP 934*, G. L. McClure, Ed., American Society for Testing and Materials, Philadelphia, 1987, pp. 131–154.

ABSTRACT: This paper discusses the issues related to the development of a practical infrared spectroscopic method for the determination of the principal types of serum lipids, triglycerides, cholesteryl esters, and phospholipids. Earlier papers on this subject are noted, and the various matrix mathematical approaches used previously for this application are compared. The results described in this work were obtained with a least squares curve fitting type of algorithm, termed a **Q**-matrix approach. Comparisons are made between results obtained with a number of different methods constructed for use with the **Q**-matrix approach.

KEY WORDS: lipid, phospholipid, triglyceride, tripalmitin, lecithin, cholesterol, phosphatidylcholine, cholesteryl, serum, ester, carbonyl, sphingomyelin, quantitative, infrared, multicomponent, linear regression, least squares, spectral, matrix inversion, overdetermined, underdetermined, biological, dimensional constraints, **K**-matrix, **P**-matrix, **Q**-matrix, correlation computerized, analysis, calibration, determination, biomedical, risk factor, weighting function, absorbance noise, signal to noise ratio.

The improvement in recent years in both the hardware and software for computerized infrared spectroscopic analysis have tended to make this type of analysis a much more attractive tool for difficult quantitative and qualitative measurements. The growth in the interest in infrared analysis of biological systems is illustrative of this point [1–6]. The objective is to translate improvements in analytical technologies into advances in the un-

[1] Senior staff scientist, senior applications chemist, and senior staff scientist, respectively, Perkin-Elmer, Corp, Norwalk, CT 06859-0903.

[2] Assistant professor, Department of Clinical Chemistry, School of Applied Health Professions, State University of New York, Stony Brook, NY 11794.

derstanding of biological systems, and ultimately into positive developments in the control of illnesses. Computerized infrared analysis appears likely to find occasion to play an increasingly important role in the study of biological and biomedical questions which may eventually amount to matters of life and death.

Disorders of lipid metabolism lead to a variety of illnesses and may become, directly or indirectly, the cause of death. Consequently, convenient analytical methods for detecting and monitoring lipid disorders are important to clinical chemists. Although many lipid disorders are linked to anomalies in the lipoproteins, analyses for the three principal classes of lipids isolated from blood serum, triglycerides (T), cholesteryl esters (C), and lecithin type phospholipids (L), can provide a convenient means for detection of a number of disorders of lipid metabolism [7].

To date, the routine determination of the major lipids such as triglycerides and cholesteryl esters has been performed generally by indirect methods, which involve ester hydrolysis and determination of glycerol and cholesterol, respectively. On the other hand, the determination of phospholipids has not been done routinely, because it is not known to correlate with an established risk factor for illness or disease. This has stemmed in part from the fact that a convenient routine method for the determination of phospholipids in serum has not been available to many clinical chemists. Consequently, determination of phospholipids has not been usually included along with the determination of triglycerides and cholesteryl esters in clinical studies, and there is a relative dearth of information on phospholipids for purposes of studying correlations with other possible risk factors.

There is evidence which could be interpreted to suggest that phospholipids may play a critical role in the deposition of substances on arterial walls [8]. Such deposition may be related to processes involved in atherosclerosis and coronary occlusion. This possibility further strengthens the need for a convenient, rapid, accurate instrumental method for the determination of phospholipids, as well as triglycerides and cholesteryl esters.

It is the principle thesis of this work that infrared spectroscopy, combined with the appropriate data handling hardware and software, is an effective method for the simultaneous determination of the three classes of lipids mentioned previously, over the range of physiological relevant concentrations.

Experimental

All spectra were recorded on a Perkin-Elmer Model 1800 Fourier transform infrared spectrophotometer (FT-IR) fitted with a 2 mm fast response deuterated triglycyine sulfate detector (FR-DTGS). All spectral data files were saved on 13.3 cm (5.25 in.) floppy disk and were based on 64 scans of the sample beam and 32 scans of the reference beam in a double beam mode with the CDS-3 software. The CDS-3 software operates on the Model 7500 laboratory computer, which controls and communicates with the optical module of the Model 1800 system. Parameters for the operation of the Model 1800 FT-IR in the quantitative mode are shown in Table 1. A double beam scan cycle is defined to be composed of 2 scans in the front beam, 2 scans in the back beam, and 2 additional scans in the front beam. The advantage of double beam operation is that it provides a means of obtaining spectral data which is ratioed against a background which includes the effects of changing water vapor concentration and other short-term variations. This feature enables almost real time compensation for variables such as those mentioned and minimizes errors in the data needed for quantitative analysis.

All quantitative calculations were carried out by means of the QUANT-3 software package for quantitative analysis by a least squares curve fitting approach (**Q**-Matrix Method). The QUANT-3 software is written to operate on the Perkin-Elmer Series 7000 professional computers, as is also the CDS-3 software. The calculation time of each analysis was approximately 0.5 min. An additional 0.5 min period was required for the first analysis to be carried out with a particular method in order to retrieve the data of the standard spectra from disk.

Omnisolve grade chloroform (CX1054) was obtained from MC&B, Cincinnati, Ohio. Lipids were obtained from Sigma Chemical, St. Louis, Missouri, and consisted of the following items: tripalmitin (T-5888), cholesteryl palmitate (C-9378), and L-alpha-dipalmitoylphosphatidylcholine, lecithin (L-6138).

Relatively concentrated stock solutions (6 g/L) of each of the three lipids were prepared in chloroform. Analytical solutions were prepared from the stock solutions by the addition of weighed aliquots of the stock solutions and dilution to the final volume (25 mL) with chloroform. Concentrations of the lipids in the solutions used for spectroscopic measurements were controlled to fall in the approximate range anticipated for actual serum samples (50 to 200 mg/dL or 0.5 to 2 g/L).

TABLE 1—*Instrument mode parameters used to acquire lipid spectra.*

Range	1850 to 850 cm^{-1}
Nominal resolution	4 cm^{-1}
Spectrum type	real
Phase correction	self, 128 points
Mirror velocity	0.25 cm/s
Acquire mode	double beam
Number of cycles	16
Cycle format	2 scans front beam
(double beam)	2 scans back beam
	2 scans front beam
Jacquinot stop	5
(aperture, 6 = largest)	
Gain	auto (3 steps of grain ranging)

Spectra were collected of sample solutions which were introduced into a 1.0-mm infrared sealed cell made with barium fluoride windows. Minstac (registered) fittings, Luer to Minstac adapters made of Kel-F and 0.16 cm (1/16) in. PTFE (polytetrafluoroethylene) tubing were attached to the syringe ports on the front of the cell to allow operation of the cell in a flow-through configuration. Such fittings are available as an infrared flow-through cell kit from The Lee Company, Westbrook, Connecticut 06498. Each of the two PTFE tubes connected to the infrared cell were run out of the instrument sample compartment, between the sample compartment bulkhead and the sliding cover. A 10-mL syringe was attached to the tube which led to the upper port of the infrared cell. Each successive sample was introduced into the cell by inserting the PTFE tubing attached to the lower port of the infrared cell into the volumetric flask which held the desired sample. The sample was drawn from the flask, through the infrared cell, and into the 10 mL syringe. In this manner the cell and connecting tubing could be purged of the previous sample and filled with the current sample without opening the sample compartment or moving the sample cell in its mount. A total of 12 to 15 mL of the sample was used for the flushing and filling the cell between samples. After each change of sample the new sample was allowed to equilibrate to the temperature of the sample compartment for 4 min before the spectral data were collected.

Results and Discussion

General Features of Infrared Spectra of Lipids

The simultaneous determination of multiple components by spectroscopic techniques depends on the fact that no two of the components to be analyzed have exactly the same spectrum. In the midinfrared spectral region from 4000 to 400 cm^{-1}, compounds with different structures and functional groups generally have quite different spectra. The different structures of the three model compounds used in this study are shown in Fig. 1. Each of the three lipids is a fatty acid ester. In addition, each of these compounds contains distinguishing functional groups. The result is that the spectra of the three types of serum lipids show a large amount of similarity, but also show some distinguishing features. The solvent subtracted absorbance spectra of chloroform solutions of the three model compounds are shown in Fig. 2 over the range from 2000 to 850 cm^{-1}. The spectral regions between approximately 1180 to 1250 and 920 to 930 cm^{-1} have been blanked out due to totally absorbing bands of the solvent.

Each of the spectra contains a carbonyl band in the 1700 to 1800 cm^{-1} region and other differentiating features at lower frequencies. The absorbance maximum of each of the carbonyl bands occurs at a slightly different frequency, but there is so much overlap of the bands that mixtures of the lipid compounds may show only a single broad band without individual

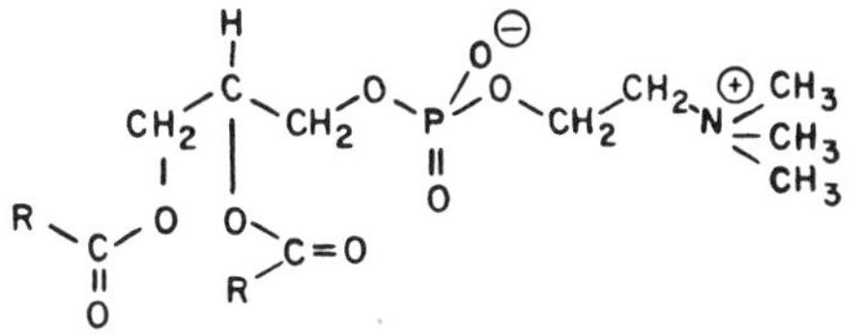

Dipalmitoyl Phosphatidyl Choline, $R = C_{15}H_{31}$
a lecithin

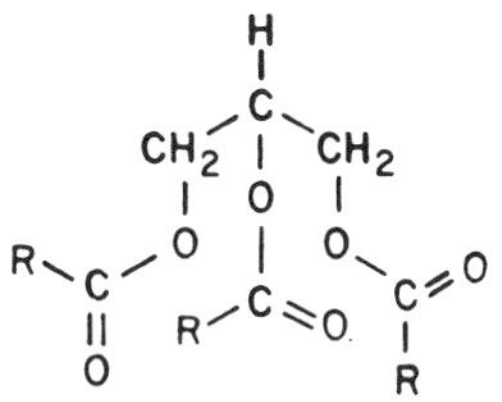

Tripalmitin, $R = C_{15}H_{31}$
a triglyceride

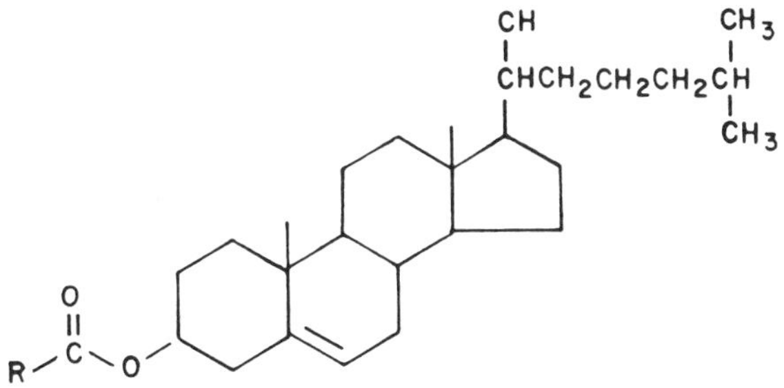

Cholesteryl Palmitate, $R = C_{15}H_{31}$
a cholesteryl ester

FIG. 1—*Structures of the three lipids used in this study.*

absorbance maxima due to the individual components. This is evident in the set of experimental mixtures used in this study, the spectra of which are shown in Fig. 3. The difference spectra of the samples with the solvent subtracted are shown in Fig. 4. The spectral regions between approximately 1180 to 1230 and 920 to 930 cm^{-1} have been blanked out due to totally absorbing bands of the solvent. These spectra show the actual absorbance variations in the sample spectra due to the lipids. The point is that many features of the lipid spectra are somewhat masked by the bands of the chloroform solvent. However, the masking does not cancel their value for quantitative purposes, as is shown by the results to be discussed.

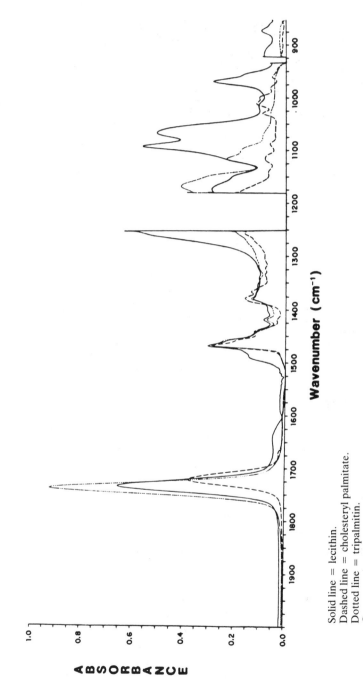

Solid line = lecithin.
Dashed line = cholesteryl palmitate.
Dotted line = tripalmitin.
Concentrations are approximately 6 g/L or 600 mg/dL.
FIG. 2—*Absorbance difference spectra of the three lipids used in this study (chloroform solvent spectrum subtracted).*

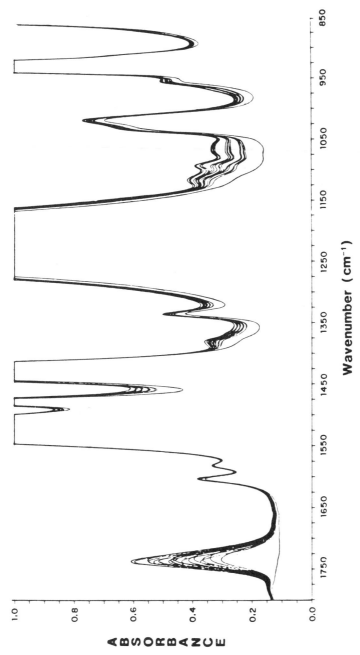

FIG. 3—*Absorbance spectra of lipid mixtures used in this study.*

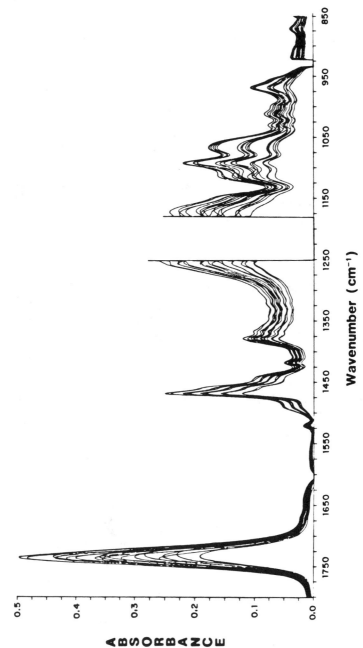

FIG. 4—*Absorbance difference spectra of the lipid mixtures used in this study (chloroform solvent spectrum subtracted).*

Above 2000 cm^{-1}, each of the lipid infrared spectra show strong bands due to carbon-hydrogen stretching absorptions. However, the lipid spectra are also quite similar in this region, because most of the absorbance arises from fatty acid side chains present in all three lipids. Consequently, the region above 2000 cm^{-1} was not further investigated in this study.

Mathematical Approaches to Dealing with Spectral Overlap

General Considerations of Multicomponent Analysis of Lipids—Beer's law can be applied in matrix form to allow the simultaneous determination of multiple components even when there is no unique set of spectral features for each of the components, that is, when there is no one band of one of the system components which is not overlapped by one or more of the bands from another of the system components. As mentioned previously, the analysis of the three major classes of serum lipids represents a condition in which the degree of overlap is quite high throughout the midinfrared region. When the data is relatively error free, quantitative calculations which involve matrix mathematics may proceed satisfactorily despite a high degree of overlap. Conversely, moderate electronic noise and instrument photometric errors can be better tolerated when the degree of spectral overlap is relatively low. However, data errors play an increasingly detrimental role on quantitative accuracy as the degree of spectral overlap increases. Consequently, it is understandable that the serum lipid analysis by infrared is relatively sensitive to data errors such as noise and instrument artifacts, because of the high degree of spectral overlap. Earlier workers observed these difficulties and regarded this analysis as "difficult if not impossible" by infrared methods [7]. In view of the fact that this perspective was offered before the general availability of microprocessor based infrared instruments, the statement was probably justified for its day.

As will be shown subsequently, the difficulties in this analysis can be overcome with a high quality spectrometer and a quantitative algorithm which facilitates the incorporation of the spectral information from a substantial range of infrared frequencies. This type of algorithm has been used for a wide variety of applications [9–13], and may be considered a curve-fit type of quantitative calculation. Although each of the matrix mathematical approaches discussed has been described previously in the literature, it is worthwhile reviewing the key aspects in order to clarify some of the features which differentiate each approach. The row and column dimensions of each matrix have been written discretely as subscripts for each matrix in the equations in order to emphasize properly the impact of dimensional factors.

*The **K**-Matrix Approach*—The direct application of Beer's law in matrix form is sometimes referred to as the **K**-matrix approach [15]. The **K**-matrix approach has been applied over a very limited range of relative concentrations to the analysis of the three serum lipids [16]. The **K**-matrix approach proceeds from the relationship shown in Eq 1, with the understanding that, for a system of N components to be analyzed, the spectra of M standard mixture samples is used for calibration, and the spectra of both standard and unknown samples must be recorded at W wavenumber locations in each spectrum.

$$\mathbf{A}_{WM} = \mathbf{K}_{WN} * \mathbf{C}_{NM} \qquad (1)$$

where

$\mathbf{A}_{WM}$ = matrix of calibration absorbance data,
$\mathbf{C}_{NM}$ = matrix of calibration concentration data, and
$\mathbf{K}_{WN}$ = absorption coefficient matrix.

The **K**-matrix approach is regarded as the "classical" least squares treatment of data for spectroscopic analyses [13]. The actual mechanics of the calculations in the **K**-matrix approach involve two steps, the calibration step and the determination or predictive step. The inversion of an **N** by **N** matrix is required in each step. The form of the equations and dimensional limitations of the **K**-matrix approach are of the following

$$\mathbf{K}_{WN} = \mathbf{A}_{WM} * \mathbf{C}_{MN}^{T} * (\mathbf{C}_{NM} * \mathbf{C}_{MN}^{T})^{-1} \qquad \text{Calibration Step} \qquad (2)$$

where

$\mathbf{C}_{MN}^{T}$ = transpose of the concentration data matrix of the standard samples, and
$(\mathbf{C}_{NM} * \mathbf{C}_{MN}^{T})$ = **N** by **N** matrix that must be inverted in the calibration step.

Dimensional Constraint: M standard mixtures $\geq N$ components or else the system is underdetermined.

$$\mathbf{D}_{N1} = (\mathbf{K}_{NW}^{T} * \mathbf{K}_{WN})^{-1} * \mathbf{K}_{NW}^{T} * \mathbf{U}_{W1} \qquad \text{Determination Step} \qquad (3)$$

where

$\mathbf{D}_{N1}$ = column vector of N concentration values determined,
$\mathbf{U}_{W1}$ = column vector of W absorbance values of the unknown sample, and
$(\mathbf{K}^{T} * \mathbf{K}_{NW})_{WN}$ = **N** by **N** matrix that must be inverted in the determination or predictive step.

Dimensional Constraint: W spectral data points $\geq N$ components or else the system is underdetermined.

When M or W is greater than N, this is referred to as overdetermination with respect to standard mixtures or spectral measurement points respectively. The advantage of overdetermination is that more than the minimum amount of information is available to solve the equations and the error in the solution is minimized by the "least squares fitting" of the data.

The P-Matrix Approach—An alternative method of calculation is the **P**-matrix approach in which the Beer's law equation in inverted to express concentration as a function of absorbance. Some of the consequences of this inverse arrangement of Beer's law have been discussed by Haaland [13]. Although the **P**-matrix approach requires only one matrix inversion, there are additional dimensional constraints placed on the data required to perform the analysis, as explained next. The fundamental equation of the **P**-matrix approach is shown in Eq 4.

$$\mathbf{C}_{NM} = \mathbf{P}_{NW} * \mathbf{A}_{WM} \tag{4}$$

where

$\mathbf{A}_{WM}$ = matrix of the calibration absorbance data,
$\mathbf{C}_{NM}$ = matrix of the calibration concentration data, and
$\mathbf{P}_{NW}$ = matrix which interconverts $\mathbf{C}_{NM}$ and $\mathbf{A}_{WM}$.

The matrix inversion required in the **P**-matrix approach is involved in the calibration step in which the **P**-matrix is calculated, as shown in Eq 5.

$$\mathbf{P}_{NW} = \mathbf{C}_{NM} * \mathbf{A}_{MW}{}^{T} * (\mathbf{A}_{WM} * \mathbf{A}_{MW}{}^{T})^{-1} \quad \text{Calibration Step} \tag{5}$$

where

$\mathbf{A}_{MW}{}^{T}$ = transposed matrix of the calibration absorbance data, and
$(\mathbf{A}_{WM} * \mathbf{A}_{MW}{}^{T})$ = **W** by **W** matrix which must be inverted.

Dimensional Constraint: M standard mixtures $\geq W$ spectral data points or the system is underdetermined.

$$\mathbf{D}_{N1} = \mathbf{P}_{NW} * \mathbf{U}_{W1} \quad \text{Determination Step} \tag{6}$$

where

$\mathbf{D}_{N1}$ = column vector of N concentration values determined, and
$\mathbf{U}_{W1}$ = column vector of W absorbance values of the unknown sample.

Dimensional Constraint: None computationally, although practically $M \geq N$ and $W \geq N$ for physically meaningful results.

The dimensional constraints of the **P**-matrix method have certain consequences. The immediate difficulty is that for every incremental point in the spectrum which is to be included in the calculation, the dimension of the matrix to be inverted increases by one. Increasing the dimension of the matrix to be inverted means that more steps are required in the calculation of the inverse, and there is a greater susceptibility to calculation error due to truncation or round off error by computer, which would tend to lead to greater probability of numerical instability in the calculations. In addition, increasing the number of spectral data points also requires an increase in the number of calibration standards to be prepared such that M can remain greater than or equal to W, in order to calculate the **P**-matrix. The consequence of this situation is that it is relatively difficult with the **P**-matrix method to use any significant portion of the infrared spectrum of samples in quantitative calculations.

It should be noted that the dimensional constraints of the **P**-matrix approach become an advantage in applications in which many standards are required to statistically characterize the system and in which the useful spectral information can be restricted to relatively few data points. An example is the determination of protein or moisture in foods [17,18].

The use of the **P**-matrix method has been described in the analysis of the three serum lipids [19]. The general trend was observed that the more spectral measurement points used in the calculation, the better the results. The authors noted difficulty in the calibration process except when a relatively large number of calibration standards were used.

*The **Q**-Matrix Approach, Least Squares Curve-Fit Quantitative Analysis*— A third form of simple multiple linear regression exists, which may be described as a curve-fit type of quantitative analysis. Haaland has classified this type of calculation as "classical" [13], despite the fact that the mechanics of the calculation and the dimensional constraints are somewhat different from the **K**-matrix approach described previously. To clearly differentiate the various methods, let this third alternative be referred to as the **Q**-matrix approach. The fundamental hypothesis of the **Q**-matrix approach is that the spectrum of an unknown mixture can be synthesized from a linear combination of the spectra of the components included in the mixture. The mathematical expression of this is shown in Eq 7.

$$\mathbf{U}_{W1} = \mathbf{A}_{WM} * \mathbf{Q}_{M1} \qquad (7)$$

where

$\mathbf{U}_{W1}$ = spectrum of the unknown sample,
$\mathbf{A}_{WM}$ = matrix of spectral data obtained from the set of calibration standards, and
$\mathbf{Q}_{M1}$ = column vector of coefficients which provides the least squares fit of the unknown spectrum by the standard spectra.

This is conceptually the reverse of the process of multiple spectral subtraction, in which the spectra of the respective components are subtracted from the spectrum of the mixture with the appropriate factors until the final residue spectrum is composed of just noise. The scaling factors in such a case are related to the elements of the **Q**-matrix. Within the limits of this description the idea of concentration does not enter into the initial least squares solution of Eq 7. The form of the generalized inverse solution for the **Q**-matrix is shown in Eq 8. This equation has some of the properties of both a calibration and a determination step, because there is a least squares fitting which involves the absorbance data of the standards, and values are determined which depend directly on the absorbance data of unknown sample.

$$\mathbf{Q}_{M1} = (\mathbf{A}_{MW}{}^T * \mathbf{A}_{WM})^{-1} * \mathbf{A}_{MW}{}^T * \mathbf{U}_{W1} \qquad (8)$$

where

$$\mathbf{A}_{MW}{}^T = \text{transposed matrix of the calibration absorbance data,}$$
and
$(\mathbf{A}_{MW}{}^T * \mathbf{A}_{WM}) = \mathbf{M}$ by $\mathbf{M}$ matrix which must be inverted.

Dimensional Constraint: W spectral data points $\geq M$ standard mixtures or the system is underdetermined.

The form of Eq 8 is identical to that found in the determination step of the **K**-matrix approach. In the special case that the matrix **C** of concentration data on the standard samples is an identity matrix, that is, standard mixtures are made from pure components with unity concentration, the absorbance matrix **A** would become numerically equivalent to the **K**-matrix, and the **Q**-matrix would become numerically equivalent to the **D**-matrix of determined concentration values in the unknown sample. This hypothetical situation occurs only rarely in practice, and another method is required to transform the **Q**-matrix coefficients into chemically meaningful concentration values. Moreover, pure materials are generally less suitable than mixtures for infrared quantitative analysis because of the issue of Beer's law nonlinearity due to molecular interactions. When mixtures are used as standards, the Beer's law nonlinearities are effectively incorporated into the solution of the **Q**-matrix. Spectra of standard mixtures which have the composition most similar to the unknown sample may become the largest coefficients in the **Q**-matrix because they best model all of the spectroscopic phenomena associated with the composition of the unknown sample.

The values of the component concentrations in the unknown sample are easily derived from the **Q**-matrix by multiplying the **C**-matrix as in Eq 9.

$$\mathbf{D}_{N1} = \mathbf{C}_{NM} * \mathbf{Q}_{M1} \qquad (9)$$

where

$\mathbf{C}_{NM}$ = matrix of the standard sample concentration data, and
$\mathbf{D}_{N1}$ = column vector of N concentration values determined.

Dimensional Constraint: None mathematically, although practically $M \geq N$ and $W \geq N$ for physically meaningful results.

Equations 8 and 9 can be combined for a direct solution of the concentration values to be determined, without a discrete solution for the values of the $\mathbf{Q}$-matrix, as shown in Eq 10.

$$\mathbf{D}_{N1} = \mathbf{C}_{NM} * (\mathbf{A}_{MW}{}^T * \mathbf{A}_{WM})^{-1} * \mathbf{A}_{MW}{}^T * \mathbf{U}_{W1} \qquad (10)$$

Incorporating Weighting Functions—The preceding discussion has shown how a large amount of spectral data can be incorporated into a compact single step solution of the concentration values in an unknown sample. Theoretically, Eq 11 implies that the matrix inversion need be calculated only once and that a matrix $\mathbf{Z}$ could be defined such that the matrix $\mathbf{D}$ could be obtained directly by multiplying $\mathbf{Z}$ by $\mathbf{U}$, as in Eq 12.

$$\mathbf{Z}_{N1} = \mathbf{C}_{NM} * (\mathbf{A}_{MW}{}^T * \mathbf{A}_{WM})^{-1} * \mathbf{A}_{MW}{}^T \qquad (11)$$

$$\mathbf{D}_{N1} = \mathbf{Z}_{NW} * \mathbf{U}_{W1} \qquad (12)$$

In practice, there is a very good rationale for not carrying out the calculations directly in this manner. Different parts of the standard and unknown spectra contain different amounts of information and noise and artifact in different regions of the wavenumber scale and the absorbance scale. Obviously, the analyst would like to weight the data points which represent high spectral information to noise ratio more heavily than those which do not. Noise is generally constant over the transmittance scale in most infrared instruments. However, when spectral data is converted to absorbance, noise produces an increasingly detrimental impact on absorbance measurements as the absorbance value increases. Consequently, a weighting function which minimizes the effects of absorbance noise at large absorbance values would be a useful modification to the fundamental equation of the $\mathbf{Q}$-matrix approach.

Haaland has proposed the use of a weighting function based on the square of the transmittance spectrum of the unknown sample, on the basis of a statistical rationale [12]. Ford and Spragg compared a variety of weighting functions for the $\mathbf{Q}$-matrix type of calculation and concluded that the first power of the transmittance spectrum of the unknown sample would provide essentially the same analytical results in most applications [20]. The data obtained in this study support the importance of a weighting function. In all examples described in this work, the weighting function was formed from the first power of the transmission values of the spectrum with the lowest transmission value in the frequency range prescribed in the respective method table. The low transmission values in the data set used were produced by the chloroform bands, which were essentially the same in all spectra. Consequently the weighting functions involved in these calculations were essentially the same for each sample within a given method.

A weighting function can be incorporated into Eq 7 from above by right side multiplication of both sides by a square matrix F with dimensions W by W. All elements of F will be equal to zero, except the diagonal elements which are the W-values of the weighting function. With a weighting function F included, the fundamental equation of the Q-matrix method is shown in Eq 13.

$$\mathbf{F}_{WW} * \mathbf{U}_{W1} = \mathbf{F}_{WW} * \mathbf{A}_{WM} * \mathbf{Q}_{M1} \tag{13}$$

where

$\mathbf{F}_{WW}$ = diagonal matrix of W transmittance values of the spectral data of the unknown sample.

If the weighting function is written to indicate its incorporation into the U and A absorbance matrices in Eq 13, then the form of the resulting equation, shown in Eq 14, is effectively identical to that shown in Eq 7. Therefore the solution of the Q- and D-matrices is the same, as shown in Eqs 15 and 16. The only limitation is that, for every new unknown sample, the new weighting function will have to be incorporated with the A and U matrices, and a new matrix inversion will have to be carried out as indicated in Eqs 15 and 16.

$$(\mathbf{F} * \mathbf{U})_{W1} = (\mathbf{F} * \mathbf{A})_{WM} * \mathbf{Q}_{M1} \tag{14}$$

$$\mathbf{Q}_{M1} = (\mathbf{A}_{MW}^T * (\mathbf{F} * \mathbf{A}_{WM})^{-1} * \mathbf{A}_{MW}^T * (\mathbf{F} * \mathbf{U})_{W1} \tag{15}$$

$$\mathbf{D}_{N1} = \mathbf{C}_{NM} * (\mathbf{A}_{MW}^T * (\mathbf{F} * \mathbf{A})_{WM})^{-1} * (\mathbf{A}_{MW}^T * (\mathbf{F} * \mathbf{U})_{W1}) \tag{16}$$

Mann and co-workers compared the results of a correlation algorithm and a least squares curve fitting approach for the analysis of the three serum lipids over a range of physiologically relevant concentrations [14]. Although satisfactory results were obtained with both methods of calculation, the results with the least squares curve fitting approach were reported to be somewhat better when the data had a high signal to noise ratio. The results described in this paper extend the investigation of the least squares curve fitting, or Q-matrix, approach for the analysis of the three types of lipids. The effects of a weighting function and variations in the spectral range of the data included in the calculations are compared.

TABLE 2—Method parameters.

	Method 1	Method 2	Method 3	Method 4	Method 5	Method 6	Method 7	Method 8
Spectral range	1800 to 833	1800 to 833	1800 to 833	1800 to 833	1800 to 1650	1778 to 1667	1783 to 1713	1800 to 853
Weighting function	T	T	none	none	T	T	T	T
Blanked regions	1622 to 1592	none	none	1250 to 1180	none	none	none	1622 to 1592
	1538 to 1505			932 to 922				1545 to 1496
	1436 to 1414							1483 to 1471
	1265 to 1168							1274 to 1164
	935 to 918							939 to 917
								859 to 853

*Lipid Analysis Data Obtained with the **Q**-Matrix Approach*

Table 2 shows the essential parameters which were varied in each of the methods investigated. Each method was operated as a four component analysis by including the solvent as a component along with the three lipids. A level baseline was included in the set of standard spectra used internally in the software to solve for the least squares fit of the unknown spectrum. The inclusion of the baseline spectrum provides a means to include any variations in the data related to shifts in the spectrum 100% line. Inspection of the data in Fig. 3 shows that no such shifts occurred during acquisition of this set of data. The baseline spectrum was included in this instance only arbitrarily as a routine precautionary measure.

The solvent concentration was entered nominally as unity for each standard, since the solvent concentration was essentially the same in all samples. Of the 18 independently prepared lipid mixture solutions, a subset of 6 were selected for use as standards for analysis of the other samples by each of the methods. Sample 5 was discarded because of an error detected in the sample preparation procedure. The remaining 11 samples were used as the unknowns to evaluate each method. Table 3 shows the lipid concentrations in the 6 samples which were used as standards.

Table 4 shows the results of the analysis of the serum lipid samples by the eight different methods described in Table 2. Table 5 shows the values of the error parameters calculated for each component by each method. The equations used to calculate the error parameters shown in Table 6.

The operation of Method 1 includes spectral data over the range from 1800 to 853 cm^{-1} except for those regions in which solvent bands cause the absorbance values to rise above a threshold of 1.5 A. (Let upper case A represent absorbance units as is the common convention). In addition the region around 1600 cm^{-1} is excluded since this is a region of absorption by water in chloroform. Traditionally, it has been recommended that quantitative absorbance measurements be restricted to values below about 0.7 A. The inclusion of values of up to 1.5 A in this method would be a cause for concern were it not for two intervening factors. First, the data on which these analyses have been carried out are derived from relatively high signal

TABLE 3—*Concentrations of lipids in standard mixtures used for calibration.*

Sample No.	Lecithin, mg/dL	Tripalmatin, mg/dL	Cholesteryl Palmitate, mg/dL
4	56.736	181.24	133.71
6	59.186	67.356	195.85
8	115.50	123.30	68.241
11	115.78	123.14	188.89
13	179.92	184.71	68.169
15	191.92	69.617	126.89

TABLE 4—*Determined concentrations.*

Sample No.		Calculated Concentration	Method 1	Method 2	Method 3	Method 4	Method 5	Method 6	Method 7	Method 8
Sample 1	L	59.834	58.383	58.210	60.702	58.518	60.890	60.992	62.363	58.339
	T	183.97	183.66	183.66	169.74	183.56	182.19	182.10	181.31	183.64
	C	64.659	65.443	65.367	114.58	65.025	64.290	64.221	63.746	65.473
Sample 2	L	57.085	56.055	55.846	59.347	56.119	58.134	58.392	60.491	56.040
	T	120.40	120.69	20.63	100.77	120.45	119.51	119.24	118.15	120.67
	C	70.866	71.279	71.378	139.52	71.585	70.308	70.181	69.325	71.304
Sample 3	L	58.632	58.669	58.535	59.330	58.298	59.556	59.818	58.772	58.678
	T	60.461	60.737	60.553	47.507	60.558	60.038	59.536	60.209	60.727
	C	128.67	128.46	128.75	176.33	128.93	127.97	127.86	128.69	128.46
Sample 7	L	119.30	118.61	118.58	121.81	119.23	119.75	119.78	121.82	118.56
	T	182.94	183.28	183.41	158.53	183.24	182.68	182.74	181.60	183.29
	C	70.701	71.526	71.365	170.04	71.435	70.889	70.896	69.595	71.520
Sample 9	L	119.20	119.61	119.60	123.89	118.72	118.64	118.70	120.71	119.65
	T	58.275	58.550	58.223	34.281	58.546	58.953	58.661	57.630	58.546
	C	131.85	131.24	131.81	216.62	131.59	131.59	131.55	130.90	131.23

Sample										
Sample 10	L	120.03	119.76	119.62	118.34	119.41	119.75	119.73	121.23	119.75
	T	184.50	184.48	184.48	168.60	184.73	184.52	184.66	183.84	184.49
	C	126.60	126.60	126.57	196.32	125.95	126.63	126.66	125.77	126.61
Sample 12	L	119.01	118.57	119.32	111.17	118.93	118.58	118.66	118.44	119.61
	T	60.645	60.875	60.634	55.474	60.635	61.414	61.180	61.314	60.887
	C	196.95	196.98	197.38	248.01	197.31	197.38	197.38	197.70	196.98
Sample 14	L	181.54	181.77	181.69	174.32	181.69	181.07	181.05	181.24	181.79
	T	128.49	128.31	128.20	115.30	128.27	128.79	128.81	128.82	128.31
	C	70.140	69.856	70.062	149.94	70.089	70.205	70.239	70.022	69.848
Sample 16	L	177.98	178.87	179.08	187.55	179.05	178.27	177.89	179.53	178.86
	T	181.22	182.19	182.30	176.13	182.42	182.53	182.92	181.88	182.21
	C	129.28	129.62	129.43	131.06	128.88	130.01	130.11	128.85	129.62
Sample 17	L	183.59	184.76	184.95	183.46	185.80	183.74	183.16	183.25	184.76
	T	124.39	123.87	123.91	142.92	123.91	124.47	125.02	125.02	123.86
	C	204.11	204.45	204.28	134.70	203.89	204.92	205.16	204.35	204.48
Sample 18	L	177.18	177.84	177.79	168.78	179.05	177.67	177.41	176.52	177.82
	T	63.911	63.906	63.917	78.549	63.299	64.004	64.373	64.843	63.933
	C	209.88	210.59	210.51	182.70	210.86	210.76	210.87	210.94	210.58

TABLE 5—*Statistical parameters.*

		Method 1	Method 2	Method 3	Method 4	Method 5	Method 6	Method 7	Method 8
MD1 mg/dL	L	0.66	0.73	4.2	0.83	0.56	0.59	1.3	0.69
	T	0.31	0.28	15.2	0.35	0.60	0.76	1.0	0.31
	C	0.41	0.32	59.0	0.45	0.46	0.54	0.72	0.42
MD2 %	L	0.68	0.76	3.2	0.77	0.67	0.75	1.5	0.71
	T	0.27	0.19	15.2	0.31	0.56	0.70	0.87	0.28
	C	0.43	0.34	59.9	0.42	0.37	0.44	0.73	0.44
SE1 mg/dL	L	0.82	0.93	5.6	1.1	0.66	0.75	1.8	0.84
	T	0.42	0.43	17.2	0.49	0.84	0.99	1.3	0.42
	C	0.52	0.43	67.8	0.55	0.57	0.66	0.89	0.53
SE2 %	L	0.66	0.74	4.5	0.91	0.53	0.60	1.4	0.68
	T	0.34	0.35	14.0	0.41	0.69	0.81	1.1	0.35
	C	0.41	0.34	53.1	0.43	0.44	0.52	0.70	0.41
CD1	L	0.999 90	0.999 88	0.987 94	0.999 84	0.999 89	0.999 91	0.999 44	0.999 88
	T	0.999 94	0.999 94	0.932 40	0.999 92	0.999 77	0.999 67	0.999 57	0.999 94
	C	0.999 93	0.999 97	0.206 04	0.999 91	0.999 94	0.999 92	0.999 92	0.999 92
SE3 mg/dL		1.18	1.24	78.46	1.52	1.36	1.58	2.66	1.27

TABLE 6—*Error parameter equations.*

Mean Absolute Deviation, mg/dL	Relative Mean Absolute Deviation, %
$$MD1 = \frac{\sum\limits_{i=1}^{J} |C_i - D_i|}{J}$$	$$MD2 = \frac{100*\sum\limits_{i=1}^{J} \frac{|C_i - D_i|}{Ci}}{J}$$
Standard Error of Estimate, mg/dL	Relative Standard Error of Estimate, %
$$SE1 = \left(\frac{\sum\limits_{i=1}^{J} (C_i - D_i)^2}{J - 1}\right)^{1/2}$$	$$SE2 = 100*\left(\frac{\frac{\sum\limits_{i=1}^{J} (C_i - D_i)^2}{J - 1}}{\frac{\sum\limits_{i=1}^{J} C_i}{J}}\right)^{1/2}$$
Coefficient of Determination	Combined Standard Error of Estimate
$$CD = \frac{\sum\limits_{i=1}^{J} (C_i - \overline{D})^2}{\sum\limits_{i=1}^{J} (D_i - \overline{D})^2}$$	$$SE3 = \left(\frac{\sum\limits_{n=1}^{N}\sum\limits_{i=1}^{J} (C_i - D_i)^2}{N * (J - 1)}\right)^{1/2}$$

NOTE—J = Number of Samples Analyzed (11).
N = Number of Components Varying (3).
C_i = Expected Concentration in Sample i.
D_i = Determined Concentration in Sample i.
$\overline{D}$ = Average of Determined Concentrations.

to noise spectra, such that the absorbance noise is relatively low. Second, Method 1 includes a transmittance weighting function which tends to suppress the contribution of high absorbance values from the calculation. The transmittance weighting function is effectively the spectrum of the solvent in each case. This results from the fact that the samples analyzed are relatively dilute, and the solvent contributes the most to the observed absorbance over most of the spectral data ranges used in the calculations. The exceptions to this are any methods which include only the carbonyl region (approximately 1800 to 1600 cm^{-1}), where the solvent bands are relatively weak. Table 5 shows that the results for Method 1 are quite good on the 11 samples analyzed, with relative standard error values (SE2) below 1% for each of the lipids.

The significance of this suppression by the transmittance weighting function of absorbance noise contributed by high absorbances can be seen in Methods 2 and 3, in which no blanked regions are included. This means that numerous absorbance values above even 5.0 A are to be included in the analytical calculations. It is clear from the error results on Method 3 in Table 5 that the results have become unreliable with no weighting function and no blanked regions, and this is as expected. In contrast, the results from

Method 2 with no blanked regions are still quite good, and relative standard error values (SE2) are still below 1% for each of the lipids.

Another interesting comparison may be made between the results in Method 3 and in Method 4. Blanked regions are used in Method 4 to exclude those regions in which strong solvent bands carry the absorbance values above 2.5 A. No transmittance weighting function is involved in either Method 3 or Method 4. While the results of Method 3 are essentially unreliable, the error parameters of Method 4 are only slightly larger than those obtained in the more conservatively designed Method 1. The results of Method 4 would not be as good were it not for the very high linearity of response of the instrument used to obtain the data and the high signal to noise achieved in the data. It is worth noting that the total time for the acquisition of the double beam spectra on the Model 1800 was around 4 min, the transmittance noise in the spectra was on the order of 0.005% transmittance root mean square (%T rms) or below. With these conditions, even with absorbance values of 2.5 A allowed in Method 4, the relative standard error values (SE2) were below 1% for each of the three lipids.

The question arises as to whether it is always better to use as much of the spectrum as possible in the curve-fit quantitative analysis algorithm, or whether a minimum subset of the spectral data exists which will give optimum results. This is too broad a question to be exhaustively investigated here. However, it is worthwhile comparing the results of Method 1 and Method 5. The results obtained with Method 5 were based on the restricted range of the spectral data from 1800 to 1650 cm^{-1}, essentially the carbonyl region. The error parameters for lecithin are somewhat smaller in Method 5 relative to Method 1. However, the respective error parameters for tripalmitin are consistently worse by about a factor of 2 for both types of standard error values calculated. Despite this, all values of relative standard deviation calculated for Method 5 are below 1%.

The results of carrying out the analysis with a more restricted data set than the 151 points used in Method 5 are shown in Table 5 for Methods 6 and 7 which use 102 and 15 spectral points, respectively, to sample the carbonyl region. It is not meant to be implied that quantitative accuracy depends directly on the number of points used in the calculation. However the results suggest the obvious, that more spectral information is generally better than less for purposes of determining components which have highly overlapped spectral features.

The results of Method 8 relative to Method 1 suggest the same trend as was observed in Methods 5, 6, and 7 in terms of the value of increasing spectral information used in the calculation. Method 8 was constructed to exclude absorbance values above 1.0 A from the calculation as blanked regions. The original hypothesis was that the results might improve relative to Method 1, in which absorbances above 1.5 A were excluded from the calculation as blanked regions. However, a comparison of the error parameters in Table 5 show that the results are slightly worse in the more conservatively designed Method 8 than in Method 1. This implies that the accuracy of the quantitative calculation benefits from the information contained between 1.0 and 1.5 A. This does not mean that data above 1.0 A would improve quantitative calculations under conditions of higher noise and less linear response of the instrument. However, it is testimonial to the quality of the spectral data which can be produced with modern instruments, and the results suggest that it is not necessary to restrict all quantitative measurements arbitrarily to the traditional working absorbance range between 0.3 and 0.7 A in all cases [21].

Overall the results tend to support the value of the use of as much of the information in the spectrum as possible as long as the effects of absorbance noise can be suppressed with a weighting function and blanked regions. For high overlap applications, such as the serum lipid analysis, this trend in the data would also tend to support the value of an algorithm which facilitated the incorporation of as much of the spectral information as possible without adversely affecting numerical stability in the calculation by ballooning the size of the matrix which must be inverted.

Conclusions and Perspectives

The results discussed previously indicate that the three major types of serum lipids, triglycerides, cholesteryl esters, and lecithin type phospholipids, can be determined with high precision in chloroform solutions by computerized infrared spectroscopy. However, this represents only the first step in pursuit of the original objective, which was to be able to determine the concentration of these materials in blood samples. There are a number of complicating factors which a successful, practical clinical infrared method for the determination of these components will have to handle. Some of these are the following:

1. The chain lengths of all of the esterified fatty acids in serum samples will not be uniform.
2. Unsaturated as well as saturated fatty acids will be present in real serum samples.
3. Other phospholipids besides lecithins will be present in serum real samples, for example sphingomyelin.
4. Some serum cholesterol is not esterified and will not be included in a determination keyed to cholesteryl esters.
5. Free fatty acids as well as mono- and diglycerides are also present in serum and must be accounted for in a multicomponent matrix method of analysis.
6. Serum itself is a very complicated fluid and some form of solvent extraction will probably be necessary to restrict the number of total variables in the samples to a relatively small number, perhaps 6 to 12.

Although this list constitutes a substantial set of possible error sources, there is reason to expect that each of these issues can be handled satisfactorily. Practically the same issues have arisen in the analysis of lipids in amniotic fluids by computerized infrared spectroscopy, and some of the present authors have published work which describes techniques available for dealing with some of the factors listed [22,23]. The magnitude of the contribution of each of these factors will have to be evaluated experimentally. Further work on the infrared analysis of serum lipids will be discussed in future publications.

References

[1] Winters, S., Gendereau, R. M., Lehninger, R. I., Jacobsen, R. J., *Applied Spectroscopy,* Vol. 36, 1982, p. 404.

[2] Dluhy, R. A., Mendelson, R., Casal, H., and Mantsch, H., *Biochemistry,* Vol. 22, 1983, p. 1170.

[3] Dluhy, R. A., Cameron, D., Mantsch, H., and Mendelson, R., *Biochemistry,* Vol. 22, 1983, p. 6318.

[4] Mendelson, R., Brauner, J., Faines, L., Mantsch, H., and Dluhy, R. A., *Biochemical Biophysics Acta,* Vol. 774, 1984, p. 237.

[5] Mendelson, R., Anderle, G., Jaworsky, M., Mantsch, H., Dluhy, R. A., *Biochemical Biophysics Acta,* Vol. 775, 1984, p. 215.

[6] Steer, C. J., Vincent, J. S., and Levin, I. W., *Journal of Biological Chemistry,* Vol. 259, 1984, p. 8052.

[7] Freeman, N. K., *Blood Lipids and Lipoproteins,* G. J. Nelson, Ed., Wiley, New York, 1972, pp. 113–179.

[8] Gershfeld, N. R., *Science,* Vol. 204, 1979, p. 506.

[9] Blackburn, J. A., *Analytical Chemistry,* Vol. 37, 1965, p. 1000.

[10] Antoon, M. K., Koenig, J. H., and Koenig, J. L., *Applied Spectroscopy,* Vol. 31, 1977, p. 518.

[11] Haaland, D. M. and Easterling, R. G., *Applied Spectroscopy,* Vol. 34, 1980, p. 539.

[12] Haaland, D. M. and Easterling, R. G., *Applied Spectroscopy,* Vol. 36, 1982, p. 665.

[13] Haaland, D. M., Easterling, R. G., and Vopica, D. A., *Applied Spectroscopy,* Vol. 39, 1985, p. 73.

[14] Tyson, L. L., Ling, Y. C., and Mann, C. K., *Applied Spectroscopy,* Vol. 38, 1984, p. 663.

[15] Brown, C. W., Lynch, P. F., Obremski, R. J., and Lavery, D. S., *Analytical Chemistry,* Vol. 54, 1982, p. 1472.

[16] Kisner, H. J., Brown, C. W., and Kavarnos, G. J., *Analytical Chemistry,* Vol. 54, 1982, p. 1479.

[17] Birth, G., *Journal of Food Science,* Vol. 44, 1979, p. 949.

[18] Geladi, P., MacDougall, D., and Martens, H., *Applied Spectroscopy,* Vol. 39, 1985, p. 491.

[19] Kisner, H. J., Brown, C. W., and Kavarnos, G. J., *Analytical Chemistry,* Vol. 55, 1983, p. 1703.

[20] Ford, M. A. and Spragg, R. A., personal communication, unpublished data.

[21] Weitkamp, H. and Barth, R., *Einfuehrung in die quantitative Infrarot Spektrophotometrie,* Georg Thieme Verlag, 1976.

[22] Lehmann, C. A. and McClure, G. L., *Analytical Letters,* Vol. 17(B7), 1984, p. 599.

[23] Lehmann, C. A., McClure, G. L., and Danielson, L. A., *Clinical Physiology and Biochemistry,* Vol. 2, 1984, p. 184.

Edmund R. Malinowski[1]

Application of Target Factor Analysis to Quantitative Absorption Spectroscopy

REFERENCE: Malinowski, E. R., **"Application of Target Factor Analysis to Quantitative Absorption Spectroscopy,"** *Computerized Quantitative Infrared Analysis, ASTM STP 934*, G. L. McClure, Ed., American Society for Testing and Materials, Philadelphia, 1987, pp. 155–168.

ABSTRACT: Factor analysis is a mathematical tool for solving multidimensional problems, having great potential in absorption spectroscopy. It can be used for both qualitative and quantitative analysis of mixtures. Abstract factor analysis reveals the number of absorbing components in a mixture, calculates the real error in the measurements, and improves the data. The method can be used to compress libraries of spectroscopic data into its smallest dimensions without loss of information. Target factor analysis allows the analyst to verify the presence or absence of suspected components. Spectra of unstable intermediates can be isolated. Various examples are discussed.

KEY WORDS: factor analysis, multidimensional analysis, principal component analysis, absorption spectroscopy, infrared spectroscopy

Factor analysis is a mathematical tool for solving multidimensional problems, having great potential in infrared spectroscopy [1]. This paper focuses attention on some of the general principles of the methodology with examples taken from various areas of chemistry as well as infrared spectroscopy.

Factor analysis is applicable to those situations in which data, d_{ik}, can be represented as a linear sum of product terms, r_{ij} and c_{jk}, such that

$$d_{ik} = \sum_{j=1}^{n} r_{ij}c_{jk} \tag{1}$$

where the sum is taken over n factors responsible for the data. In matrix notation Eq 1 becomes

$$[\mathbf{D}] = [\mathbf{R}][\mathbf{C}] \tag{2}$$

[1]Professor of Chemistry, Department of Chemistry and Chemical Engineering, Stevens Institute of Technology, Hoboken, NJ 07030.

where d_{ik}, r_{ij}, and c_{jk} are the elements of matrices [**D**], [**R**], and [**C**]. Factor analysis, essentially, breaks data matrix [**D**] into a product of two matrices, [**R**] and [**C**], called the row and column matrices.

In infrared spectroscopy, according to Beer's law, the absorbance, A_{ik}, (per unit pathlength of mixture k at wavelength i) obeys the sum of product terms

$$A_{ik} = \sum_{j=1}^{n} e_{ij}c_{jk} \tag{3}$$

where

e_{ij} = molar absorptivity per unit pathlength of component j at wavelength i, and

c_{jk} = molar concentration of component j in the kth mixture.

Thus factor analysis is suitable for the analysis of complicated mixtures *via* their infrared spectra. Some of the problems that can be solved with factor analysis are the following:

1. Determine the number of absorbing components.
2. Isolate the spectra of the unknown components.
3. Measure the concentration of each component.

The main steps in factor analysis are illustrated in Fig. 1. The first series of steps leading to "short-circuit reproduction" is called abstract factor analysis (AFA). These steps are based on the mathematics of principal component analysis. The covariance matrix, [**Z**], is constructed by premultiplying the data matrix by its own transpose. This matrix is decomposed into linear factors which reproduce the data. These steps define the coordinates of the factor space, reveal the true dimensions of the factor space,

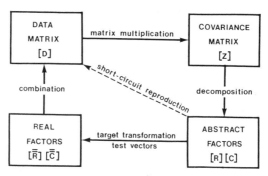

FIG. 1—*Main steps in factor analysis* [*Reprinted with permission from E. R. Malinowski and D. G. Howery,* Factor Analysis in Chemistry, *Wiley-Interscience, New York, 1980*].

and yield mathematical, abstract, solutions for [R] and [C] which are devoid of any physical meaning. These abstract factors account for the original data within experimental error *via* the short-circuit reproduction and can be used empirically to predict new data without regard to any physical understanding of the chemistry involved.

Target factor analysis (TFA) is used to transform these abstract solutions into physically significant, chemically recognizable solutions, $[\bar{\bar{R}}]_{real}$ and $[C]_{real}$. This is accomplished by finding a transformation matrix [T] such that

$$[\bar{\bar{R}}]_{real} = [R][T] \tag{4}$$

$$[\bar{\bar{C}}]_{real} = [T]^{-1}[C] \tag{5}$$

One of the exciting features of factor analysis is that, under certain conditions, these matrices can be obtained from the data matrix alone, without any *a priori* information.

Abstract Factor Analysis

The problem to be solved by factor analysis is to find [R] and [C] from a knowledge of [D]. This is accomplished by diagonalizing the covariance matrix [Z], which is defined as

$$[Z] = [D]^{T}[D] \tag{6}$$

by finding a matrix [Q] such that

$$[Q]^{-1}[Z][Q] = [\lambda] \tag{7}$$

where $[\lambda]$ is a diagonal matrix composed of eigenvalues. Each column of [Q] is called an eigenvector. These eigenvectors represent abstract axes of the factor space. One can easily show that

$$[R] = [D][Q] \tag{8}$$

and

$$[C] = [Q]^{T} \tag{9}$$

Thus the problem reduces to finding the matrix which diagonalizes the covariance matrix. This is automatically accomplished by a mathematical method called principal component analysis.

The theory of error for abstract factor analysis [2] shows that the size of the eigenvalue measures the relative importance of the associated eigenvector. The eigenvalues can be divided into two groups called primary and secondary. The large primary eigenvalues contain chemical information with a mixture of experimental error. The small secondary eigenvalues contain nothing but experimental error. If the data contained no experimental error the secondary eigenvalues would be equal to zero, and there would be no problem in determining the exact size of the factor space. Unfortunately, obtaining perfectly pure, error free, data are beyond our expectations. So we must devise methods for deciding which eigenvectors belong to the primary set.

The root-mean-square (RMS) difference between the raw data and the hypothetically pure data is called the real error (RE). The RMS difference between the AFA reproduced data and the hypothetically pure data is called the imbedded error (IE). The RMS difference between the raw data and the AFA reproduced data is the extracted error (XE), that is, the amount of error that is removed upon deleting the secondary eigenvectors. Although we can never "see" the pure data matrix, these errors can be estimated by means of the following expressions obtained from the theory of error [2]

$$RE = \left[\frac{\sum_{j=n+1}^{c} \lambda_j}{r(c - n)} \right]^{1/2} \tag{10}$$

$$IE = RE \, [n/c]^{1/2} \tag{11}$$

$$XE = RE \, [(c - n)/c]^{1/2} \tag{12}$$

where

r and c = number of rows and columns of the data matrix,
n = number of factors, and
λ_j = j^{th} eigenvalue, the sum being taken over all error eigenvalues.

In these equations it is assumed that $r > c$; if $r < c$ then r and c must be interchanged.

These three error terms are related in a Pythagorean fashion, as illustrated in Fig. 2, namely

$$(RE)^2 = (IE)^2 + (XE)^2 \tag{13}$$

Because the imbedded error, IE, is always less than the real error, RE, this relationship predicts that AFA reproduced data will always be more accurate than the original data, a fringe benefit of abstract factor analysis. Koenig and co-workers [3] used this fact to reduce the noise level in the infrared spectra of polymers.

To determine the number of factors responsible for the data [4], the factor analyst calculates RE as a function of n, and then chooses n to be that for

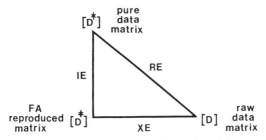

FIG. 2—*Mnemonic diagram of the Pythagorean relationship of the errors in abstract factor analysis* [*Reprinted with permission from E. R. Malinowski,* Analytical Chemistry, *Vol. 49, 1977, p. 606*].

which RE is closest to the error estimated by the experimentalist. If an accurate error estimation is not available, one can examine the IE which tends to level off when an excessive number of factors is employed. The factor indicator function (IND) has been surprisingly successful in picking out the correct number of factors. This empirical function is defined as

$$\text{IND} = \text{RE} \, (c - n)^{-2} \tag{14}$$

The IND is a minimum when the true number of factors is used.

Cross validation, devised by Wold [5], is another valuable method for determining the number of factors. This method consists of deleting a row of the data matrix, performing AFA, and then TFA using the deleted row as the target. This sequence is repeated until every row of the data matrix has been deleted and target tested. The standard deviations of the target rows are then calculated as a function of n, the number of abstact eigenvectors employed in the target tests. As n increases the standard deviation will decrease if the additional eigenvector is primary. There will be no further decrease in the standard deviation upon the addition of secondary eigenvectors.

This procedure is time consuming because it requires a complete eigenanalysis and target test for each row of the data matrix. The process can be speeded up greatly by binary cross validation which involves separating the data matrix into two submatrices, one composed from the even rows and the other composed from the odd rows. AFA is conducted on one submatrix, and the rows of the other submatrix are target tested in the resulting abstract space. Then the procedure is reversed. AFA is performed on the second submatrix, and the rows of the first submatrix are target tested. The standard deviations of the combined sets of target tests are then computed.

Table 1 illustrates the usefulness of these error criteria for determining the number of components present in a series of related mixtures. Abstract factor analysis was performed on a data matrix consisting of the infrared absorbances of ten different mixtures of ortho-, meta-, and para-xylene and

TABLE 1—*Results of abstract factor analysis of the infrared absorbances of ten mixtures of ortho-, meta-, and para-xylenes, and ethylbenzene.*

n	RE	IE	IND $\times$ 10^4	SD (BCV)
1	0.06352	0.02009	7.84	0.0852
2	0.04173	0.01866	6.52	0.0710
3	0.02227	0.01220	4.55	0.0403
4	0.00110	0.00070	0.31	0.0015
5	0.00096	0.00068	0.39	0.0015
6	0.00085	0.00066	0.53	0.0014
7	0.00078	0.00065	0.86	0.0013
8	0.00069	0.00062	1.74	0.0016
9	0.00067	0.00063	6.66	0.0021

ethylbenzene recorded at 35 wavenumbers from 682 to 818 cm^{-1} at 4 cm^{-1} intervals [6]. The spectroscopist estimated the experimental error to lie somewhere between 0.001 and 0.002 absorbance units. Notice that the real error (RE) equals 0.00110 at $n = 4$, giving evidence for four absorbing components. This conclusion is confirmed by the fact that at $n = 4$ the IE value levels off, the IND function reaches a minimum, and the standard deviation SD (BCV) obtained from binary cross validation levels off.

There are many other methods for deducing the dimensions of the factor space. As pointed up by Duewer, Kowalski, and Fasching [7], various criteria, examined together, afford a better guide than reliance on a single rule.

Storing large libraries of spectra in computers presents a serious problem because of storage limitations. Isenhour and co-workers [8] used AFA to compress a library of 2300 vapor phase infrared spectra into a 37 factor space without any loss of resolution upon short-circuit reproduction (see Fig. 1). Each spectrum was digitized at 185 discrete wavenumbers from 750 to 3500 cm^{-1}. Although the complete library contained 425 500 (2300 $\times$ 185) absorbance points, only 91 945 ((2300 $\times$ 37) + (37 $\times$ 185)) points associated with the abstract row and column matrices needed to be stored. This represents a 78.4% reduction in required storage capacity without any loss of discriminatory power. Furthermore, the speed with which the AFA regenerated spectra could be obtained was found to be faster than any other compression technique known today.

Target Factor Analysis

In spite of the complexity of the factor space, target factor analysis (TFA) allows us to test theoretical and hypothetical concepts, *individually*, without requiring any knowledge of the other contributing factors [9]. This powerful aspect of TFA is quite different from regression analysis which requires specification of all factors simultaneously, which in many chemical problems is a serious stumbling block. In TFA we search for a transformation vector, T_j, such that

$$\bar{R}_j = [R]T_j \tag{15}$$

where $\bar{R}_j$ is the predicted vector that lies in the factor space, emulating, as close as possible, the real factor suspected of being responsible for the data. The transformation vector is obtained by carrying out the following least-squares computation

$$T_j = \{[R]^T[R]\}^{-1}[R]^T\bar{\bar{R}}_j \tag{16}$$

where $\bar{\bar{R}}_j$ is the target vector.

Unfortunately, errors in the target mix with errors from the data matrix, confusing the target testing procedure. The theory of error for target factor analysis [9], after simplification, shows a Pythagorean relationship between the RMS errors involving the target vector, $\bar{\bar{R}}_j$, the predicted vector, $\bar{R}_j$, and the hypothetically pure vector, $\bar{\bar{R}}_j{}^*$. As illustrated in Fig. 3, the RMS difference between the raw target vector and the TFA predicted vector is the apparent error in the target (AET); the RMS difference between the raw target vector and the hypothetically pure target is the real error in the target (RET); and the RMS difference between the predicted vector and the pure target is the real error in the predicted vector (REP). These three RMS errors are related as follows

$$(\text{AET})^2 = (\text{RET})^2 + (\text{REP})^2 \tag{17}$$

According to the theory of errors the real error in the predicted target comes predominantly from the data matrix and can be approximated by the following equation

$$\text{REP} = \text{RE}(T_j \cdot T_j)^{1/2} \tag{18}$$

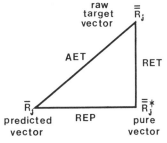

FIG. 3—*Mnemonic diagram of the Pythagorean relationship of the errors in the target test vector* [*Reprinted with the permission from E. R. Malinowski,* Analytical Chimica Acta, *Vol. 103, 1978, p. 339*].

where RE, recall, is the real error in the data matrix, and $T_j \cdot T_j$ is the dot product of the transformation vector. Since AET is obtained directly from the target test, Eq 17 can be used to estimate RET, the real error in the target.

To judge whether or not a suspected target lies in the factor space we examine the SPOIL of the target defined as

$$SPOIL = RET/REP \qquad (19)$$

The SPOIL is a measure of how well the target fits inside the factor space [9]. Similar to the 3σ-test in statistics, a SPOIL greater than 3 means that the vector does not fit well inside the factor space, whereas a SPOIL less than 3 indicates that the vector lies in the factor space. Recognizing that each column of the data matrix lies inside the factor space, we can determine the SPOIL cutoff criterion for a given data matrix by examining the SPOILS obtained from target testing each data column.

Table 2 shows the results of target testing the infrared spectra of pure compounds suspected to be components of the ten mixtures described in the previous section [6]. These results are based on four factors, as deduced from Table 1. Ortho-, meta-, and para-xylene, and ethylbenzene are identified as the components because their SPOIL values are small, whereas chloroform, toluene, and 1,2,4-trimethylbenzene are ruled out because their SPOILS are extremely large.

In an elaborate study Isenhour and co-workers [10] used similar tests, based on Bessel's inequality, to correctly identify ten components of a mixture by target testing a library of some 904 vapor-phase spectra. The data matrix for this study was generated by recording the FTIR spectra at selected time intervals during a gas-chromatographic scan.

Spectral Isolation

Lawton and Sylvestre [11] were the first to isolate the spectra of components from mixed spectra by a method based on the principles of factor

TABLE 2—Results of target testing the infrared spectra of pure compounds suspected to be components of the ten mixtures in Table 1 (based on four factors).

Target Compound	AET	REP	RET	SPOIL	Component?
o-xylene	1.96	0.57	1.88	3.30	yes
m-xylene	0.72	0.58	0.42	0.72	yes
p-xylene	0.83	0.57	0.60	1.07	yes
ethylbenzene	1.30	0.59	1.16	1.97	yes
chloroform	201.0	1.13	201.0	180.0	no
toluene	66.6	0.53	66.6	130.0	no
1,2,4-trimethylbenzene	36.6	0.02	36.6	1600.0	no

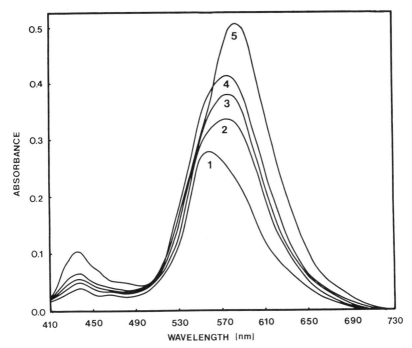

FIG. 4—*Visible spectra of five mixtures of standard dyes* [*Reprinted with the permission from W. H. Lawton and E. A. Sylvestre*, Technometrics, *Vol. 13, 1971, p. 617*].

analysis. By digitizing the visible spectra of five mixtures of standard dyes (Fig. 4) at 10 nm intervals they generated an absorption matrix that could be reproduced within experimental error using only the first two principal eigenvectors. Thus the mixtures contained only two absorbing compounds.

The results of abstract factor analysis [1] are displayed in Fig. 5. The eigenvectors, labelled C_1 and C_2, represent orthogonal axes of the two-dimensional factor space. The mixtures (data columns 1, 2, 3, 4, and 5) are nonorthogonal axes that lie inside the factor space. The coordinates of these axes are the values of the abstract column factor matrix [$\mathbf{C}$]. Each wavenumber (data row) is a point in factor space. The coordinates of these points are the values of the abstract row factor matrix [$\mathbf{R}$]. These points are plotted in Fig. 5. The perpendicular projection of any row point onto any data column is the value of the data point in the absorbance matrix.

Because the absorbance of a pure component is a product of its absorptivity and concentration, positive quantities, all points and data column vectors must be subtended between the true component axes. If each component has a unique absorption wavenumber, then the component axes must pass through these points. The axes labelled $\bar{C}_1$ and $\bar{C}_2$ in Fig. 5 fulfill these requirements. The spectrum of each component can be isolated by obliquely projecting the wavenumber point onto these two axes. The results of such projections are shown in Fig. 6.

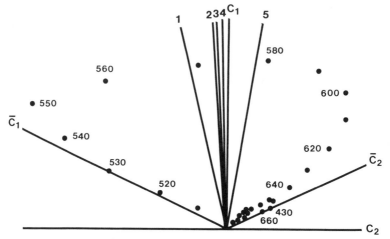

FIG. 5—*Results of abstract factor analysis of spectra shown in Fig. 4, after digitization* [*Reprinted with permission from E. R. Malinowski and D. G. Howery,* Factor Analysis in Chemistry, *Wiley-Interscience, New York, 1980*].

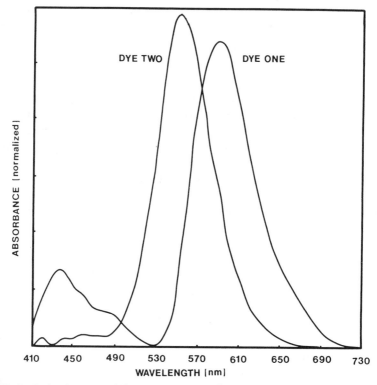

FIG. 6—*Isolated spectra of the pure components* [*Reprinted with permission from W. H. Lawton and E. A. Sylvestre,* Technometrics, *Vol. 13, 1971, p. 617*].

The self-modeling method of Lawton and Sylvestre [11] was restricted to two-component systems. Knorr and Futrell [12] extended the method to more than two components and a further improvement was made by Malinowski [13] who introduced the principle of maximum orthogonality. Each wavenumber row of the abstract row factor matrix is normalized so the sum of squares across each row equals unity. This places every row point on the surface of a semihypersphere in factor space. The pure component axes are the most orthogonal set of normalized row vectors. This set of axes is called the key set. The method of determinants used to obtain this set is called key set analysis [13].

The exciting feature about key-set spectral isolation is that it affords us a method, albeit under restrictive conditions, for extracting the spectra of unstable intermediates that cannot exist outside the system because of the controlling chemical equilibria. An excellent example of this is the Raman spectra of aqueous sulfuric acid. Malinowski, Cox, and Haldna [14] factor analyzed the spectra of 16 solutions ranging from 0.0087 to 0.9723 acid mole fraction recorded from 230 to 1380 cm^{-1}. The spectra were digitized into 96 wavenumbers, yielding a 96 × 16 data matrix. Abstract factor analysis showed the presence of three major components, with a real error of 13%.

Key-set analysis [14] was performed on a subset of the data. Wavenumbers (rows) containing mostly noise, with average signals less than five times the real error, were deleted because row normalization gives equal weight to all points, treating noise rows as real data. Inclusion of noise rows could lead to false solutions. Key-set analysis of the subset identified wavenumbers 1146, 1024, and 982.5 cm^{-1} as being most unique to each of the three unknown components. Oblique projections of all 96 wavenumber points onto these three axes yielded the unconnected spectra shown in Figs. 7, 8, and 9.

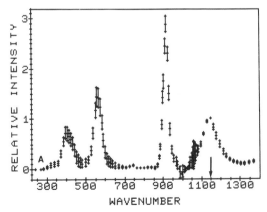

FIG. 7—*Unconnected, isolated Raman spectrum of component A with unique intensity at 1146 cm^{-1} (see arrow). Vertical bars represent uncertainties [Reprinted with permission from E. R. Malinowski, R. A. Cox, and U. L. Haldna, Analytical Chemistry, Vol. 56, 1984, p. 778].*

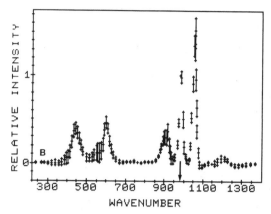

FIG. 8—*Unconnected, isolated Raman spectrum of component B with unique intensity at 982.5 cm^{-1} (see arrow). Vertical bars represent uncertainties [Reprinted with permission from E. R. Malinowski, R. A. Cox, and U. L. Haldna,* Analytical Chemistry, *Vol. 56, 1984, p. 778].*

The vertical bars associated with each point in the isolated spectra represent the uncertainties determined by the method of Clifford [15] as suggested by Roscoe and Hopke [16]. The fact that all points are positive within their calculated uncertainties lends credence to the isolation.

In order to obtain the concentration matrix, each isolated spectra was used as a target vector. Equation 16 yielded the appropriate transformation vector for each component. These vectors were assembled into a matrix, and Eq 5 was then used to generate the concentration matrix. The results of this procedure are shown in Fig. 10. The concentrations are listed as relative concentrations because the isolated spectra are uncalibrated. Cur-

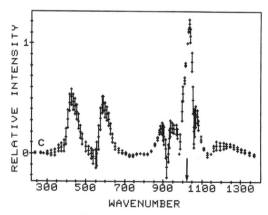

FIG. 9—*Unconnected, isolated Raman spectrum of component C with unique intensity at 1024 cm^{-1} (see arrow). Vertical bars represent uncertainties [Reprinted with permission from E. R. Malinowski, R. A. Cox, and U. L. Haldna,* Analytical Chemistry, *Vol. 56, 1984, p. 778].*

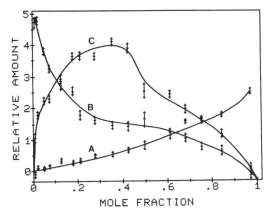

FIG. 10—*Relative (uncalibrated) concentrations of components A, B, and C of aqueous sulfuric acid. Vertical bars represent uncertainties [Reprinted with permission from E. R. Malinowski, R. A. Cox, and U. L. Haldna,* Analytical Chemistry, *Vol. 56, 1984, p. 778].*

rently we are developing techniques to provide the necessary calibration constants to convert these values into absolute units, a problem that is not trivial.

Many bands in the infrared do not obey Beer's law because of the formation of unstable species which the analyst fails to recognize. We tend to blame these failures on the instrument, the analytical procedure, or poor technique. Such failures may be due to the chemistry of the system which we do not fully understand or recognize. Factor analysis offers us a new method for isolating the spectra of unstable intermediate species.

Unfortunately the method has a severe limitation, requiring at least one unique spectral point for each contributing component. How then can we isolate the spectra when there are no unique points? This is the seemingly impossible problem that we are currently attempting to solve.

References

[1] Malinowski, E. R. and Howery, D. G., *Factor Analysis in Chemistry*, Wiley-Interscience, New York, 1980.
[2] Malinowski, E. R., *Analytical Chemistry*, Vol. 49, 1977, pp. 606–612.
[3] Gillette, P. C. and Koenig, J. L., *Applied Spectroscopy*, Vol. 36, 1982, pp. 535–539.
[4] Malinowski, E. R., *Analytical Chemistry*, Vol. 49, 1977, pp. 612–617.
[5] Wold, S., *Technometrics*, Vol. 20, 1978, pp. 397–405.
[6] McCue, M. and Malinowski, E. R., *Analytica Chimica Acta*, Vol. 133, 1981, pp. 125–136.
[7] Duewer, D. L., Kowalski, B. R., and Fasching, J. L., *Analytical Chemistry*, Vol. 48, 1976, pp. 2002–2010.
[8] Hangac, G., Wieboldt, R. C., Lam, R. B., and Isenhour, T. L., *Applied Spectroscopy*, Vol. 36, 1982, pp. 40–47.
[9] Malinowski, E. R., *Analytica Chimica Acta*, Vol. 103, 1978, pp. 339–354.
[10] Williams, S. S., Lam, R. B., and Isenhour, T. L., *Analytical Chemistry*, Vol. 55, 1983, pp. 1117–1121.

[11] Lawton, W. H. and Sylvestre, E. A., *Technometrics*, Vol. 13, 1971, pp. 617–633.
[12] Knorr, F. J. and Futrell, J. H., *Analytical Chemistry*, Vol. 51, 1979, pp. 1236.
[13] Malinowski, E. R., *Analytica Chimica Acta*, Vol. 134, 1982, pp. 129–137.
[14] Malinowski, E. R., Cox, R. A., and Haldna, U. L., *Analytical Chemistry*, Vol. 56, 1984, pp. 778–781.
[15] Clifford, A. A., *Multivariate Error Analysis*, Applied Science, London, 1973.
[16] Roscoe, B. A. and Hopke, P. K., *Analytica Chimica Acta*, Vol. 132, 1981, pp. 89–97.

Tomas Hirschfeld[1]

Computerized Infrared: The Need for Caution

REFERENCE: Hirschfeld, T., "Computerized Infrared: The Need for Caution," *Computerized Quantitative Infrared Analysis, ASTM STP 934*, G. L. McClure, Ed., American Society for Testing and Materials, Philadelphia, 1987, pp. 169–179.

ABSTRACT: So much can be done in infrared (IR) spectroscopy with computers that we are beginning to lose the healthy paranoia that should accompany their use. Even when we are careful, our precautions are quite unequal to the sophisticated and unobvious errors computers can generate. Even such apparently unobjectionable statements as "this algorithm should only be used by experts" often can be translated upon reflection to "since the program will track your prejudices, you better start with the right ones." Searching algorithms, trial and error optimizations, multilinear regressions, and factor analysis all have higher order failure modes that are briefly reviewed. Computer simulation requires far more brute force in its application than we normally employ. And the very severe problem of flow frequency bugs can be approached only by redundant algorithmic pathways.

KEY WORDS: infrared, computers, algorithm, spectroscopy, computerized IR, Fourier deconvolution

We have had the opportunity to acquire over the last few years quite a lot of confidence in the use of computers to extract all kinds of things from the infrared (IR) spectra we measured [1–5]. However, confidence alone may not be enough. Computers have been applied to bypass the limitations of our data, they have also learned to bypass most of the internal error-checking mechanisms that we have developed in our built-in organic computer. To offset this, we need to maintain a fairly diligent sense of paranoia about the results that we get from our newfangled "intelligent" machines.

To start with we must ask what it is we are trying to accomplish when we process data through a computer. The applications for which we use computers can be classified into generic categories, such as, removal of parts of our data that we do not want to see, reorganization of these data into forms that are easier to interpret by our traditional visual interpretation methods, and overcoming dynamic display limitations. The last example of the series merits further elaboration. Consider, for example, the last case. Our most

---

[1] Lawrence Livermore National Laboratory, Livermore, CA 94550.

modern instruments are capable of giving signal/noise ratios greater than 10^5 which means that if your chart paper is over 60 m tall, it would display the data appropriately. Quite obviously, the only way around this is to remove so much of the data that the significant part of it falls within the limitations imposed by the width of the ink trace and that of the paper. Subtraction of absorbance spectra is a case in point of such a procedure (Fig. 1). Two spectra that seem identical by visual observation, after substracting from each other and automatically scale expanding the difference spectrum, suddenly display all kinds of otherwise subtle features. Other examples involve procedures like Fourier deconvolution (Fig. 2). Everything that this Fourier deconvolution brings out was in the data in the first place. It is just that those little wriggles in the spectrum have now become big wriggles, without any new data being generated. What we have done is restate the data in forms in which its observability has been increased.

The common feature of all these latest algorithms for infrared spectroscopy is their ability to bring out things that we can barely see in the original data. Obviously, they are also very good at bringing out defects that we can barely see in the original data [1,6–8]. Foremost among these, of course, because of their power and relative newness, are Fourier deconvolution and factor analysis. And our old friend spectral substraction is virtually a seismograph. It will detect not only whether your sample is changed by 0.1% at some point in time, but will also seem to detect the phases of the moon and the mood you were in while you were measuring the data (Fig. 3). Most of these powerful new computer techniques tend, on very slight provocation, to give impressive looking spectral signatures which may or may not be real. The often used statement "to use algorithm x-y-z, you must know what you are doing" is, unfortunately, less meaningful than it seems. This becomes obvious when we translate it into "if you know the results in advance, this algorithm will confirm your prejudices."

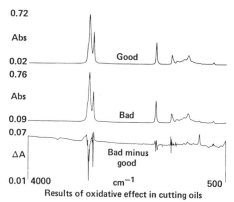

FIG. 1—*Spectral subtraction can bring out differences between spectra that would otherwise lie below our observability threshold.*

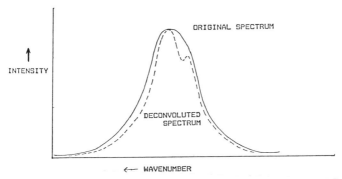

FIG. 2—*Fourier deconvolution highlights data already observable (with considerable difficulty) in the original spectrum.*

The problem is that all too often our method of checking out some extremely powerful new algorithm is to see if the results seem "reasonable" [9]. That is a terribly bad verification procedure because "reasonable" is another word for describing what we knew before the beginning of the analysis. And if we make sure of getting the results we expected to start with, what is the point of making the measurements? In fact, if all we are doing is confirming our initial prejudice, how can we be sure that the initial prejudice was right? The value of any data processing algorithm is exclusively its ability to be surprising and truthful at the same time. Unless it says something one did not expect and can be relied upon at that point, the algorithm is doing nothing useful.

What do we do when we get something that is surprising, (that is, when the data do not look right), or when we do not know what the results are supposed to look like? Then there are a number of possibilities for confirming such information. "Everybody says so" is, of course, no confirmation at all. "It looks right" should be terminated with extreme prejudice. "It repeats" only means that the data (or the calculation procedures) are either correct or afflicted by systematic error (and systematic errors are just as

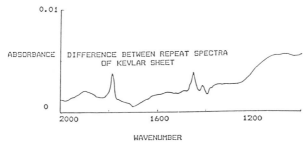

FIG. 3—*Spectral subtraction can be a very efficient (and often convincing) algorithm for creating nondata.*

abundant as random ones). Or one can start testing the algorithm. Here a few elementary levels of testing can already avoid a lot of trouble. One can add noise to the data and see how the results change. Even better, one can add noise in realistic amounts. If the data change in fundamental ways, one had better not trust these data to signify anything else either. An even better method is to check the algorithm against samples with known properties. Unfortunately, those are not that easy to come by, particularly if the method is very powerful and capable of discerning very fine details. Furthermore, one must use a great variety of these samples to test the entire envelope of the operating conditions of the method.

On the other hand, one can use simulated data generated by the computer for these tests [9,10]. However, we have not been sufficiently ambitious about this in the past. Such simulations have all too often been applied with parsimony and have rarely included simulation of a majority of the known real defects in the data. It is not enough to construct a few Lorentzians and apply a new data processing method to them. We had better add noise to the Lorentzian, then wavelength repeatability problems, wedging effects, a few interference fringes, a few resolution problems, and then see if the algorithm still works.

Beyond this, whenever one gets a real bad sample or sampling problem, one should store it in some corner of the disk as a "gallery of horrors," and when testing one's newest brainstorm in data algorithms, run through this "gallery of horrors" and see how transformed errors look. Another alternative, of course, is to develop independently different procedures addressing the same problem by different means and compare the results.

Before using new software for anything, one should thus "exercise" it with realistic synthetic spectra simulations. One can also take the real spectra containing known real or added synthetic perturbations to see the difference they will make. To create confidence, and cover a significant "operating envelope," the number of tests must be large and cover a significant range of a great many variables.

Clearly, the proper way to do this at a finite level of effort, is to construct an exercise driver, that is, a piece of software that systematically changes the perturbations, the signal level, the bandwidth, the band intensity, the noise level, etc., and then applies the algorithm and checks against the known (generated in advance) correct answer (Fig. 4). Such exercise drivers, instead of testing one, two, or five different cases, can go through a few hundred ones, and in so doing establish the new algorithm at a much higher level of confidence. There should not be too much difference in the approach used in testing a new algorithm and a new airplane. Such an exercizer algorithm will generate information not only on a method's validity and the range over which it can be applied, but will also give us information on error appearance, magnitudes, and partial derivatives for the various errors as a function of the initial problem.

BLOCK DIAGRAM OF EXERCISER SOFTWARE

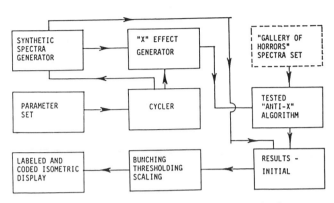

FIG. 4—*An algorithm exercizer for new algorithm development.*

When using an exercise driver as a testing method, the next problem is what to do with the miles of paper that the machine shoots out. Therefore, the exercise driver should include an automatic preconcentrator for the data, eliminating all features that do not deviate from the original. More discriminating filters here can save even more effort in interpreting the results.

Even for a computer the number of total tests required can easily get prohibitive. This number, in fact, is exponential in the resolution with which each parameter is tested and superexponential in the number of such parameters. Here we can benefit from using the simplex algorithm [11]. While these are usually applied to optimization, they can be used for worst case location by merely using the inverse of the normal quality parameter to "optimize" on. This automatically causes the simplex algorithm to search for the worst case instead of the best. And, once the worst case locations have been determined, one can set up limits for each error mechanism that will allow the new algorithm to stay away from these locations.

All of the preceding is particularly applicable to basic flaws and errors of design in any new algorithm. It also holds for problems inherent in the built-in limitations of the data. However, one must not ignore just plain mistakes (in coding, transcription, etc.). There is a fairly high frequency of bugs in a new algorithm. Unfortunately, as our algorithms get more sophisticated, such bugs may no longer be easily detected. After all, when a bug produces a result that states the sample concentration is infinite, one suspects something may be wrong. However, if it says that the concentration is 25% off, this may be plausible enough to be believed. Plausible errors in algorithms are very hard to detect (in fact, they are usually found by accident). Current experience in algorithm debugging indicates that the detection frequency of bugs decreases exponentially in time. One thing about exponentials, they do not ever quite finish dying. In fact, long past the point at which an algorithm's useful life ends because of obsolescence, bugs in it will still be appearing. An illustrative example is the HP35 calculator, the first of the pocket sliderules, which had a lifetime of about seven years in the marketplace. Eight years after its introduction somebody discovered that in calculating the arc tangent of 2.10 the HP35 gave an error of more than a factor of 2. On changing the input by even 1 in the seventh decimal place, the error disappeared. It took eight years for one of the 250 000 users to discover this. Obviously, then, one cannot check out algorithms to the point that they stop having bugs. For all we know, there still may be unknown bugs in the HP35 software. How, then are we going to cope with plausible low frequency bugs that do not show up early in the algorithm's lifetime?

Here, redundancy is clearly the way to go. A common way of making computer memories reliable, even though its components are not perfect, is to put an extra parity bit into the system and check it. Another trick is the duplication of hardware in the computer in order to make them more reliable. Well, what is wrong with duplication of software? Usually, whenever an algorithm is important enough, there will be a couple of versions circulating. It is then possible to use these in parallel to check them against each other, reducing the probability of undetected errors. While later versions of software tend to have fewer bugs, sometimes new errors appear, and the combination is thus always desirable.

Of course, the value of using multiple variations on an algorithm increases as the amount both algorithms have in common decreases. This variation can be developed by reprogramming, preferably by a different person. Even better, one can work with programs from different suppliers. Transporting software from one machine to another is becoming easier now, with the more common use of high level language programming, better machine compatibilities, and automatic translation programs. The emergence of "defacto" standards in both hardware and software will also help here. In the meantime, interesting problems can be detected by just transporting data (for which transportability standards exist now) from one machine to another and using nominally comparable arithmetic packages from different manufacturers on it. Such highly uncorrelated paths to the same solution have a very high power of verification for each other.

As instrumentation computers are eventually replaced by personal computer-based instrumentation, software compatibility, as well as the availability of multiple independent versions of any generally useful algorithm, will increase markedly. The problem of low frequency plausible algorithm bugs will then become much less worrisome than it is today.

In the foregoing, we have assumed that digital calculations are infallible and that there is no such thing as a calculation error in a digital computer. Nonsense. It was shown in the past that the number of bits per word needed to make a Fourier transform work is quite significant [11]. The demonstrated need for up to 26-bit computation was eventually met by 32-bit double precision algorithms. It is quite possible that eventually we will run into algorithms where even this is not enough (this may indeed be the case in inverse Laplace transforms).

Sometimes the bottleneck in computerized infrared spectroscopy lies in what we do not know about the infrared. We often say, for example, that an infrared spectrum is a unique characteristic of a sample. This not only has not been proven, but nobody has ever tried to prove it. In fact, it is quite easy to come up with a "Gedanken" experiment in which two different chemicals have extremely similar infrared spectra (well within the reproducibility of measurement). The infrared spectrum is a property of a molecule that is determined by short range relationships between atoms. Given a large enough molecule, one can rearrange that molecule in such a way that all the short-range relationships between atoms remain constant, and only the long-range ones move, in which case the midinfrared will show practically no change. Polymer and protein chemists often encounter such situations when looking at sequence patterns variations.

We are also in need of more knowledge about information content in infrared spectra. What is the spectral density of information as a function of wavelength? Where does the variance of an infrared spectrum concentrate? What are the wavelengths that are most chemically orthogonal? We know the fingerprint region is the best region, but that is one resolution element information. These are significant questions whose answers would enable us to design faster and more reliable search algorithms, and whose investigation has just begun [12].

Many other such questions can be studied statistically by a computer looking at reference spectral collections. Consider, for example, spectral compression. What can we remove from an infrared spectrum and still do the job? We do not really know. But we must compress the data in order to be able to do a spectral search in a finite time. In the past we deleted intensity data and everything still worked. Then we drastically reduced resolution; ditto. And then recently Clara Smith reported that when she discarded half the spectrum, she got increased hit rates in searches [13]! And this worked even when different portions of the spectrum were discarded. It turns out that we can explain this (but only post facto—somebody had to do it first!). Because an infrared spectrum is over-determined, it contains more information than what is needed for reliable identification. Taking part of the spectrum thus does not greatly reduce the ability to do an identification. But it does greatly reduce the probability of finding an impurity band (in either the sample or the reference spectrum!). In fact, in an infrared spectrum, the identification ability has saturated by the time one is using about one third or one half the data. One already has enough information, but the amount of one's disinformation still increases linearly with the length of spectrum used (Fig. 5). Thus throwing away at random part of the information can have benefits!

Data collections have interesting problems of their own. Since they take

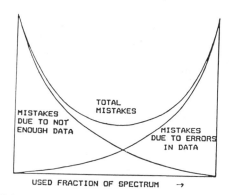

FIG. 5—*Using all the data in an infrared spectrum is not necessarily an optimal strategy.*

a long time to accumulate, they are always either too small or embody obsolete technology. For example, until a short time ago the majority of the infrared spectra collections were obtained in prism instruments (remember?). Interestingly enough, in obtaining the largest extant collection, the Sadtler library, the biggest effort involved was obtaining the samples. And no matter how many reruns one can get on ever better instruments, the samples are now an average of 15 years old. What about their instability, and, for that matter, their original quality? There is an opportunity here for a continued effort to accumulate samples and run them through "data factories" using a fast instrument and an automatic sample changer, with rapid sample preparation methods (possibly involving laboratory robotics if necessary).

Incidentally, one thing that we can do to upgrade reference data is apply factor analysis to them. When two samples are in a reference collection, one can be reasonably sure that they will not have exactly the same impurities. One can be reasonably sure also that the major component of both samples is the right one. Therefore, factor analysis will give mathematically purified spectra from the impure ones, a rapid way of cleaning up reference data collections. These problems are not minor. I would say that existing data sets have several percent error densities. Here computer errors, instrument errors, and so on, are not even the majority. Labeling errors, clerical transcription errors, failures in keeping track of which bottle was which, unsuspected problems in the sample or its preparation, are all more frequent.

In talking about error sources, our own prejudices are not unimportant either. A recent argument between two manufacturers of near infrared instruments had one saying, "One should use spectral derivatives for analysis; it is better." The other one argued for the use of spectral intensities instead. But they both used two intensities at adjoining wavelengths with equal and opposite coefficients in the calculation. This happens to be just the mathematical definition of a derivative. So the argument was really about doing the same thing with different nomenclatures. An even more common man-made error is the use of "peak-to-peak noise." We take a random phenomenon, observe it for an unstated length of time, and the maximum excursion is supposed to be an accurate value." Actually it neither has a precise mathematical meaning, nor does it propagate predictably through calculations. It is usually, but not always, a too conservative method. It may sound more conservative than root mean square (rms) noise, but it is only the latter that is meaningful in detailed error propagation calculation and, therefore, in devising and evaluating new computerized infrared techniques.

Obviously the problem is compounded by reporting "noise" without specifying which one is meant. Incidentally, while actual noise levels are important in methods development and evaluation, the measurement of noise is considerably less accurate than the measurement of the signal. In fact, if the signal accuracy varies as the square root of the number of measurements, noise accuracy varies as the fourth root (Fig. 6). Since our decisions on how to do a certain analysis or how to rate one instrument or one procedure against another are often based on noise values, this can make published comparisons unreliable unless the differences are quite marked.

Human bias is another problem, and sometimes has very sophisticated ways of sneaking into an experiment. Consider methods optimization. The

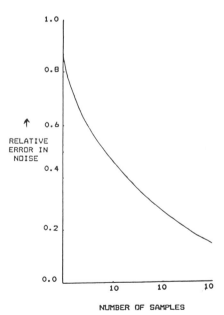

FIG. 6—*Accuracy of a noise measurement as a function of the number of points measured.*

usual approach is to compare various procedures and keep changing these, while measuring the quality of the results. We then discard any changes that make the data worse, and keep the ones that give better results.

There are a great many hidden pitfalls in this universally used guidance method for choosing an optimum procedure [14]. To start with, if successive improvement steps become small compared with the noise, the fact that there is still much improvement possible becomes undetectable because the individual steps toward that goal are no longer observable. Next, if one takes a technique that has a flaw in it and removes the flaw by a correction procedure, the data get better, does it not? WRONG. There is even a chance that removing a flaw from a procedure makes the data worse. This happens because we do not know whether the error that was just removed is of the same sign or the opposite sign as the sum of all the remaining errors. Unless one can be sure that the error being removed is far larger than the sum of the remaining errors, any correction that is real and right has an even chance of making the data worse! An approach that takes care of this problem, and of the problem of observing small individual improvement steps, is never to try out any change by itself. Instead, one should always try them out in pairs or in triads. Then the probability of getting a sign anticorrelation between the removed and the residual errors is sharply reduced, and the visibility of any improvements obtained is strongly improved.

The impression I want to leave is that there are far too many things that we are being optimistic about in computerized infrared. As we rapidly become more sophisticated in our methods, our precautions need to evolve comparably. Eventually, all new procedures developed in computerized infrared will need to be backed up with objective methods of verifying them in extenso and in detail over their entire operating envelope. For this, the same computer that got us in trouble to start with can be an invaluable tool.

Acknowledgment

This work was performed under the auspices of the U.S. Department of Energy by the Lawrence Livermore National Laboratory under contract number W-7405-ENG-48.

References

[1] Hirschfeld, T., in *Fourier Transform IR Spectroscopy,* A. Ferraro, Ed., Academic Press, New York, 1979, p. 193.
[2] Hirschfeld, T., *Analytical Chemistry,* Vol. 50, 1978, p. 1023.
[3] Kaupinnen, J. K., Moffat, D. J., Mantsch, H. H. and Cameron, D. G., *Proceedings,* SPIE, 1981, p. 260.
[4] Lowry, S. R. and Huppler, D. A., *Analytical Chemistry,* Vol. 55, 1983, p. 1288.
[5] Maaland, D. M. and Easterling, R. G., *Applied Spectroscopy,* Vol. 36, 1982, p. 665.
[6] Hirschfeld, T., *Applied Spectroscopy,* Vol. 30, 1976, p. 550.
[7] Hirschfeld, T., *Applied Spectroscopy,* Vol. 29, 1975, p. 524.

[8] Hirschfeld, T., *Research Development,* No. 7, Vol. 20, 1976.
[9] Hirschfeld, T., *Applied Spectroscopy,* Vol. 32, 1978, p. 160.
[10] Hirschfeld, T., *Applied Spectroscopy,* Vol. 31, 1977, p. 289.
[11] Foskett, C., *Applied Spectroscopy,* Vol. 30, 1976, p. 531.
[12] Delaney, M. F. and Warren, F. V., Jr., *Analytical Chemistry,* Vol. 55, 1983, p. 1925.
[13] Smith, C. D., private communication.
[14] Hirschfeld, T. and Stark, E., in *Food Analysis,* G. Charamboulous, Ed., Academic Press, New York, 1984, p. 505.

Author Index

Subject Index